# Walch Hands-on Science Series

# *Light and Color*

by W. Michael Margolin

illustrated by Lloyd Birmingham

Project editors:  Joel Beller and Carl Raab

J. WESTON
WALCH
PUBLISHER

Portland, Maine

# User's Guide
## to
## *Walch Reproducible Books*

As part of our general effort to provide educational materials that are as practical and economical as possible, we have designated this publication a "reproducible book." The designation means that the purchase of the book includes purchase of the right to limited reproduction of all pages on which this symbol appears:

Here is the basic Walch policy: We grant to individual purchasers of this book the right to make sufficient copies of reproducible pages for use by all students of a single teacher. This permission is limited to a single teacher and does not apply to entire schools or school systems, so institutions purchasing the book should pass the permission on to a single teacher. Copying of the book or its parts for resale is prohibited.

Any questions regarding this policy or request to purchase further reproduction rights should be addressed to:

Permissions Editor
J. Weston Walch, Publisher
321 Valley Street • P.O. Box 658
Portland, Maine 04104-0658

1   2   3   4   5   6   7   8   9   10
ISBN 0-8251-3760-8
Copyright © 1998
J. Weston Walch, Publisher
P. O. Box 658 • Portland, Maine 04104-0658
Printed in the United States of America

# Contents

# To the Teacher

This is one of a series of hands-on science activity books for middle school and early high school students. A recent national survey of middle school students conducted by the National Science Foundation (NSF) found that:

- more than half listed science as their favorite subject
- more than half wanted more hands-on activities
- 90 percent stated that the best way to learn science was to do experiments themselves.

The books in this series seek to capitalize on these findings. These books are not texts but supplements. They offer hands-on, fun activities that will turn some students on to science. All of these activities can be done in school, and most of them can also be done at home. The authors are teachers who have field-tested the activities in a public middle school and/or high school.

Every effort has been made to use readily available, inexpensive equipment. In cases where an experiment calls for costly equipment, alternatives are suggested for performing the activity with less sophisticated equipment. Activities range from very simple (showing that light travels in straight lines) to difficult (determining the magnification of a lens). There is something for every student. We strongly recommend that teachers try these activities themselves before asking students to perform them.

Due to the rapid and constant evolution of the Internet, some sites may no longer be accessible at the addresses listed at the time of this printing.

## THE ACTIVITIES CAN BE USED:

- to provide hands-on experiences pertaining to textbook content.
- to give verbally limited children a chance to succeed and gain extra credit.
- as the basis for class or school science fair projects or for other science competitions.
- to involve students in science club projects.
- as homework assignments.
- to involve parents in their children's science education and experiences.
- to foster an appreciation for physical science.

This book provides hands-on activities in which students:

- manipulate equipment.
- interpret data.
- evaluate experimental designs.
- draw inferences and conclusions.
- apply the methods of science.

Each activity has a Teacher Resource section that includes, besides helpful hints and suggestions, a scoring rubric, a quiz, and Internet connections for those students who wish to carry out the follow-up activities. Instructional objectives and the National Science Standards that apply to each activity are provided in order for you to meet state and local expectations.

# What Is the Nature of Light?

  **INSTRUCTIONAL OBJECTIVES**

Students will be able to
- record observations.
- identify light as a form of energy.
- draw conclusions based on observations.

**NATIONAL SCIENCE STANDARDS ADDRESSED**

Students demonstrate understanding of
- light as a form of energy.
- interactions between energy and matter.

Students demonstrate scientific inquiry and problem-solving skills by
- identifying a problem and evaluating the outcome of its investigation.
- working in teams to collect and share information and ideas.
- identifying and controlling variables in an experimental research setting.

Students demonstrate competence with the tools and technologies of science by
- using a radiometer.

 **MATERIALS**
- Radiometer
- Cardboard screen
- Flashlight

### HELPFUL HINTS AND DISCUSSION

**Time frame:** One period
**Structure:** Cooperative learning groups
**Location:** Classroom

In these activities, students make observations about the behavior of a radiometer and conclude that light is a form of energy. Students should be familiar with the definition of energy and different forms of energy prior to this activity.

### ADAPTATIONS FOR HIGH AND LOW ACHIEVERS

**High Achievers:** Encourage these students to do the follow-up activities, especially activities 2 and 4.

**Low Achievers:** Provide a glossary and reference material for boldfaced terms in this activity. Organize these students into cooperative learning groups, each of which should include students of higher ability.

### SCORING RUBRIC

Full credit should be given to students who complete observations and answer all questions correctly, using full sentences. Extra credit should be given for completing follow-up activities.

 **INTERNET TIE-INS**
http://www.solarhouse.com
http://www.winstonsolar.org
http://www.yahoo.com/science/education/
http://www.exploratorium.edu/

 **QUIZ** How does a radiometer demonstrate that light is a form of energy?

Name_____ Date _____

---

### ✤ BEFORE YOU BEGIN ✤

To begin the study of light, you are going to make some observations that will help you understand the nature of light. In these activities, it is important to remember that eyes are the sense organs that register light: We recognize light by seeing it. To understand the nature of light, you need to distinguish between energy and work. **Energy** is defined as the ability to do work. **Work** is done when an object is moved from one place to another.

---

 **MATERIALS**

- Radiometer
- Cardboard screen
- Flashlight

 **PROCEDURE**

Record your observations and answers to questions on the back of the sheet.

1. Place the radiometer on the tabletop. Describe it in words or draw a diagram. **Hypothesize** about what might make it work. How can you test your **hypothesis**?

2. Now, shine the flashlight on the radiometer and observe how the presence of light affects the behavior of the radiometer. To change the **intensity** of light, move the flashlight closer to and farther from the radiometer. Observe the results and record your observations. What is the effect of increasing and decreasing the intensity of light on the radiometer? How can you explain what took place?

3. Using the cardboard screen, block the radiometer from the light and observe the effect. Record your observations. How does blocking light from the radiometer affect it? How can you account for what took place? What evidence is there that work was done when the light hit the radiometer?

### DATA COLLECTION AND ANALYSIS

1. (a) Describe the radiometer and hypothesize about how it works.
   (b) Do the moving vanes show a form of energy? If so, what kind of energy is this?
   (c) Draw a diagram of the radiometer. Using arrows, show the direction in which light travels relative to the radiometer.
   (d) Do you think that the radiometer is doing work? Justify your answer.

2. (a) What is the effect of shining a flashlight on the radiometer?
   (b) Write a general statement about the effect of increasing and decreasing the light intensity on the radiometer?
   (c) Explain why increasing the light intensity has the effect it does on the radiometer.

*(continued)*

## What Is The Nature of Light? *(continued)*

3. (a) Record your observations of how blocking the light affects the radiometer.
   (b) Why does the radiometer slow down and eventually stop when the light is cut off?

### ❓ CONCLUDING QUESTIONS

1. Based on your observations, what can you conclude about the relationship between light and the operation of the radiometer?

   _____

   _____

   _____

   _____

2. *Energy* is defined as the ability to perform work. Considering this statement and your observations of the radiometer, support the statement that light is a form of energy.

   _____

   _____

   _____

   _____

3. Based on your observations, can you explain why a solar-powered calculator does not work in the dark?

   _____

   _____

   _____

   _____

---

### 🔦 FOLLOW-UP ACTIVITIES 🔦

1. Suggest one additional experiment to test the effect of light on the radiometer. Carry the experiment through to completion.

2. Research how solar batteries work.

3. Conduct similar experiments to observe the effect of light on a solar panel.

4. Suggest an additional experiment that would **quantify** the relationship between the distance of a light source from the radiometer and the intensity of light. Carry out this experiment to completion.

# How Can We Show That Light Travels in Straight Lines?

 **INSTRUCTIONAL OBJECTIVES**

Students will be able to
- record observations.
- demonstrate that light travels in straight lines.
- draw conclusions from observations.

 **NATIONAL SCIENCE STANDARDS ADDRESSED**

Students demonstrate understanding of
- the path in which light travels.
- interactions between light and matter.

Students demonstrate scientific inquiry and problem-solving skills by
- identifying a problem and evaluating the outcome of the investigation.

Students demonstrate effective scientific communication by
- arguing from evidence.
- explaining scientific concepts to other students.
- working individually and in teams to collect and share information and ideas.

 **MATERIALS**

- Light source
- Three pieces of cardboard with holes, mounted on wooden blocks
- Rubber hose (1 meter long)

## HELPFUL HINTS AND DISCUSSION

**Time frame:** One period
**Structure:** Individual students or cooperative learning groups
**Location:** In class or at home

Materials needed for this exercise can be purchased commercially or made by the teacher or students. Several light sources can be used. An ideal source would produce a focused beam of light that can be aimed in one direction—for example, a small flashlight on a cradle that holds it at an appropriate height and directs the beam in a straight line. If this is not available, a candle will work as light source. However, as the candle melts, it loses height. So, if you use a candle, this exercise should have a limited time frame, and you should change the candle periodically. Use a cork borer to punch a hole in each piece of cardboard Make sure that all holes are punched in exactly the same place in the cardboards, are uniform, and are of equal diameter. Remember that the height of the holes when the cardboard pieces are mounted must be compatible with the positioning of the light source so light can pass through the holes.

## ADAPTATIONS FOR HIGH AND LOW ACHIEVERS

**High Achievers:** Encourage these students to perform the follow-up activities.

**Low Achievers:** Provide a glossary and reference material for boldfaced terms in this activity. Organize these students into cooperative learning groups, each of which should include students of higher ability.

## SCORING RUBRIC

Full credit should be given to students who record observations and answer all questions correctly, using full sentences. Extra credit should be given for completing follow-up activities.

 **INTERNET TIE-INS**

http://nyelabs.kcts.org/nyeverse/l
http://www.sciencenow.org
http://www.mos.org/
http://www.odin.phys.bris.ac.uk8080
http://www.exploratorium.edu/

**QUIZ** A friend tells you that he has a great method for looking around corners. He wants to use a rubber tube that will bend around a corner and let you see things. State whether you think this will work, and give the reasons for your opinion.

If you think that this will not work, suggest some changes that might make it work.

Name_____   Date_____

# How Can We Show That Light Travels in Straight Lines?

## 🎇 BEFORE YOU BEGIN 🎇

In this activity you will perform laboratory exercises to test the statement that light travels in straight lines. You will use a light source and several pieces of cardboard, each with a hole punched in it. If light travels in a straight line, the holes will have to be lined up to let light pass through all of them. On the other hand, if light can bend, it will not be necessary to line up the holes. (See diagram.) It is important to remember that the sense organ for receiving light is your eye. You can only see an object if it is **luminous** or **illuminated**. A luminous object gives off its own light, and an illuminated object reflects light from another source. For example, if you were reading a book at your desk using a desk lamp, the lightbulb in the lamp would be luminous, and the book illuminated. Since you will be observing light, you should darken the room so that outside light does not interfere with your observations.

## MATERIALS

- Light source (lighted candle, flash-light, etc.)
- Three pieces of cardboard with holes, mounted on wooden blocks
- Rubber hose (1 meter long)

## PROCEDURE

Record your observations and answers on the back of the sheet.

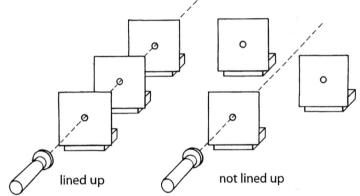

lined up          not lined up

1. Turn off the room lights. Place the first piece of cardboard in front of the light source (a luminous body) and look through the hole to see the light. Describe the relative positions of the light source, the cardboard, and your eye when you can see light passing through the hole in the cardboard. Now, continuing to look through the hole, move the cardboard to the right until you can no longer see light coming through. What characteristic of light have you demonstrated? Return the cardboard to its original position.

2. Position the second piece of cardboard so you can see light shining through the holes of both the first and second pieces. Make a drawing that shows the positions of the light source, both cardboards, and your eye when you can see light passing through the holes in both cardboards. Without changing the position of your eye, change the alignment of the cardboards so you can no longer see the light. Explain why you can no longer see the light.

3. Repeat procedure 2 with all three pieces of cardboard. Why is it necessary to add another piece of cardboard?

4. Turn the room lights back on, hold the rubber tube to your eye, and look through it. Describe how you must hold the rubber tube to see the illuminated objects in the room.

*(continued)* 🔥

## How Can We Show That Light Travels in Straight Lines? *(continued)*

 DATA COLLECTION AND ANALYSIS

1. (a) Describe the relative positions of the light source, the cardboard, and your eye when you can see light passing through the hole in the cardboard.
   (b) Draw the relative positions of the light source, the cardboard, and your eye when you can't see any light.
   (c) What characteristic of light have you demonstrated?

2. (a) Make a drawing that shows the positions of the light source, both cardboards, and your eye when you can see light passing through the holes in both cardboards.
   (b) Make a drawing to show the positions of the light source, both cardboards, and your eye when you can't see any light passing through the holes.
   (c) Explain why you can't see the light when you change the alignment of the cardboards.

3. (a) Why is it necessary to add another piece of cardboard?
   (b) Describe the relative positions of the light source, the three cardboards, and your eye when you can see light passing through the holes in all cardboards.
   (c) Describe the relative positions of the light source, the three cardboards, and your eye when you can't see any light passing through the holes.
   (d) What conditions were necessary for light to travel through the holes in the three cardboards to your eye?

4. Describe how you must hold the rubber tube to see illuminated objects through it.

 CONCLUDING QUESTIONS

1. Based on your observations, what did your experiments reveal about the nature of light?

2. Members of the drama club ask for your help in lighting the stage for a play. Their spotlight lights the wrong part of the stage. They would like to construct an apparatus to redirect the light. Sketch and describe an apparatus that will do this.

---

### ☀ FOLLOW-UP ACTIVITIES ☀

1. Research and diagram how a periscope works.

2. Research eclipses. Use your knowledge that light travels in straight lines to explain how, when, and why they occur.

3. If a bell is placed in a vacuum, it cannot be heard, because sound does not travel in a vacuum. Design an experiment to see if light can travel in a vacuum.

---

# How Can We Describe the Image in a Plane Mirror?

 **INSTRUCTIONAL OBJECTIVES**

Students will be able to

- record observations.
- describe the image in a plane mirror.
- distinguish between an object and an image.
- define the terms *image, virtual image, inverted, erect, reversed.*
- draw conclusions from observations.

 **NATIONAL SCIENCE STANDARDS ADDRESSED**

Students demonstrate understanding of

- the characteristics of the image in a plane mirror.
- interactions between light and matter.

Students demonstrate scientific inquiry and problem-solving skills by

- identifying a problem and evaluating the outcomes of its investigation.
- working individually and in teams to collect and share information and ideas.

Students demonstrate effective scientific communication by

- arguing from evidence.
- representing data and results in multiple ways.
- explaining scientific concepts to other students.

 **MATERIALS**

- Plane mirror
- Two dowels with supports
- Cardboard cutout of human figure
- Writing sample
- Metric ruler

---

### HELPFUL HINTS AND DISCUSSION

**Time frame:** One period
**Structure:** Individual students or cooperative learning groups
**Location:** In class or at home

Dowels should be cut to be 5–6 cm longer than the mirror, so that they are visible above the mirror's top edge. Supports for the dowels can be fashioned out of wood or clay. The cardboard cutout of a human figure can be prepared by students or by the teacher. Choose a photograph about 12 cm high from a magazine, cut it out, and paste it on a piece of cardboard. Trim the cardboard to follow the outline of the picture. Color the left side of the figure with a marker so that students can easily discern the left and right sides when they look at the image in the mirror. The cutout should not be taller than the mirror. Trim it or use another mirror if necessary. Use a small piece of wood or clay to fashion a stand for the cutout. The writing sample can be cut from a headline in a magazine or newspaper. The mirror can be attached to a small block of wood to stand upright on its own.

---

### ADAPTATIONS FOR HIGH AND LOW ACHIEVERS

**High Achievers:** Encourage these students to do the follow-up activities, particularly activities 1 and 2.

**Low Achievers:** Provide a glossary and reference material for boldfaced terms in this activity. Organize these students into cooperative learning groups, each of which should include students of higher ability.

---

### SCORING RUBRIC

Full credit should be given to students who record observations and correctly answer all questions, using full sentences. Extra credit should be given for completing follow-up activities.

---

 **INTERNET TIE-INS**

http://www.sciencenow.org
http://www.osa.org/aboutosa/stuchap/
http://www.yahoo.com/Science/Education/

http://www.exploratorium.edu/
http://www.mip.berkeley.edu/physics

**QUIZ**
1. If an object is placed three feet in front of a mirror, how far behind the mirror will the image in the mirror appear to be?
2. How does the image of an object in a mirror differ from the object itself? *(continued)*

Name_____ Date _____

# How Can We Describe the Image in a Plane Mirror?

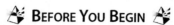 **BEFORE YOU BEGIN**

In this activity, you will explore the characteristics of the image in a mirror. When you look in a mirror, what you see there is called an **image**. Is there actually something behind the mirror? As a small child, you may have thought that there was a real person (who looked just like you!) on the other side of the mirror. What you see in a mirror is really light reflected by the mirrored surface. We say that the image in the mirror is a **virtual image**, one that appears to be real but is not.

 MATERIALS

- Plane mirror with stand
- Two dowels with supports
- Cardboard cutout of human figure colored on one side with a marker
- Writing sample with large letters
- Metric ruler

 PROCEDURE

1. Place one of the dowels 3 cm in front of the mirror. Record this distance as the Trial 1 **object distance** in the data table in the Data Collection and Analysis section.

2. Place the second dowel behind the mirror. With your eye at the top of the mirror, align the rear dowel with the image of the first dowel that you see in the mirror. The rear dowel must look as if it is an extension of the reflected image. Measure the distance from the rear dowel to the back of the mirror. Record this distance as the Trial 1 **image distance** in the data table.

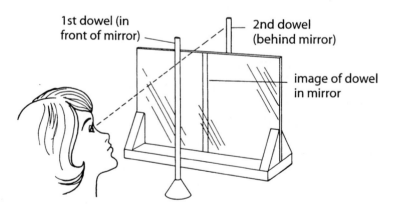

1st dowel (in front of mirror)

2nd dowel (behind mirror)

image of dowel in mirror

3. Repeat steps 1 and 2, increasing the object distance to 10 cm. Record these as Trial 2 object and image distances in the data table.

4. Repeat steps 1 and 2, this time increasing the object distance to 15 cm. Also record these object and image distances in the data table as Trial 3.

*(continued)*

## How Can We Describe the Image in a Plane Mirror? *(continued)*

Record your answers to the following questions on the back of the sheet.

5. Measure the height of the cardboard cutout of the human figure. Now hold the ruler and the cutout in front of the mirror together. How tall does the image appear to be?

6. Place the cutout in front of the mirror. Which side of the object has been colored with a marker? Which side of the image appears colored with the marker?

7. Place the writing sample in front of the mirror. Describe the appearance of the image.

 DATA COLLECTION AND ANALYSIS

### Data Table

|  | Object Distance | Image Distance |
|---|---|---|
| Trial 1 |  |  |
| Trial 2 |  |  |
| Trial 3 |  |  |

1. Compare the apparent height of the image of the human figure with the height of the object.

2. (a) Which side of the human figure has been colored?
   (b) Which side of the image appears colored?

3. Describe the appearance of the printed text as it appears in the mirror.

### CONCLUDING QUESTIONS

1. Summarize in a brief paragraph the relationship between the distance of an object from a mirror and the apparent distance of the corresponding image.

2. How does the size of the image in a mirror compare to the size of the object?

3. Were the images left-right reversed? Support your answer with observations you recorded.

4. Were the images erect or inverted? Support your answer with observations you recorded.

5. How is the word *ambulance* written on the front of ambulances? Why?

6. Some people have difficulty tying a necktie or putting on makeup while looking at their reflection in a mirror. How can you account for this?

*(continued)*

## How Can We Describe the Image in a Plane Mirror? *(continued)*

### ☙ FOLLOW-UP ACTIVITIES ☙

1. Draw a diagram that shows how a beam of light would be reflected by a mirror. Using a dotted line, extend the reflected ray behind the mirror to show where the reflected ray seems to be coming from.

2. Place two mirrors at right angles to each other and observe your reflection in this right-angle mirror. How does this reflection differ from that in a plane mirror? Draw a diagram to explain the difference in the two images.

3. Research how the wave theory of light can be used to explain reflection.

4. Many magic tricks use mirrors. Here's how you can use a mirror to fool an audience into thinking that you are pulling an object out of an empty box. Cut two doors, one in the front and one on top of a cardboard box. Place a mirror in the box at a 45° angle, so that when someone looks through the front door, the box appears empty. Place the object above the mirror; then pull it out of the top of the "empty" box. Try this magic trick.

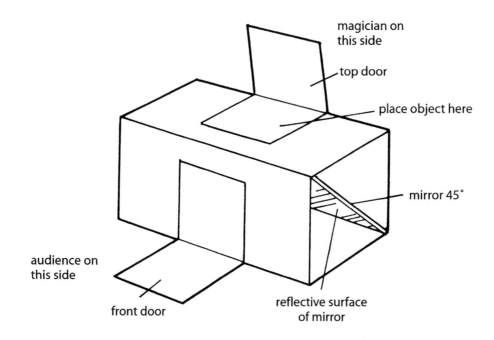

# How Do Different Materials Affect the Absorption of Light?

 ## INSTRUCTIONAL OBJECTIVES

Students will be able to

- record observations.
- define the terms *opaque* and *transparent*.
- explain that light striking a surface may be reflected, transmitted, or absorbed.
- distinguish between reflection, transmission, and absorption of light.
- draw conclusions based on observations.
- explain that light energy may be changed to heat energy.

## NATIONAL SCIENCE STANDARDS ADDRESSED

Students demonstrate understanding of

- absorption, reflection, and transmission of light by different surfaces.
- conservation of energy.
- interactions of energy and matter.

Students demonstrate scientific inquiry and problem-solving skills by

- identifying a problem and evaluating the outcomes of its investigation.
- working individually and in teams to collect and share information and ideas.
- identifying and controlling variables in an experimental research setting.
- using physical science concepts to explain observations.

Students demonstrate effective scientific communication by

- representing data and results in multiple ways.
- arguing from evidence.
- explaining scientific concepts to other students.

Students demonstrate competence with the tools and technologies of science by

- using laboratory equipment.

## MATERIALS

- Lamp with 100-watt lightbulb
- Four Erlenmeyer flasks: one black, one white, one silver, and one plain
- Four alcohol thermometers
- Four one-hole stoppers
- 100-ml graduated cylinder
- Glycerin

---

### HELPFUL HINTS AND DISCUSSION

**Time frame:** One period
**Structure:** Individual students or cooperative learning groups
**Location:** In class or at home

The materials for this exercise can be purchased commercially or made by the teacher or students. To prepare black and white flasks, paint the outside surfaces with flat paint or cover the flasks with black and white paper. The surfaces of black and white flasks should be dull. The mirrored flask can be painted silver or covered with aluminum foil. Carefully supervise students while they are inserting thermometers in stoppers. Remind students to avoid subjecting the flasks to direct light, which might raise the water temperature.

---

*(continued)*

## ADAPTATIONS FOR HIGH AND LOW ACHIEVERS

**High Achievers:** Encourage these students to do the follow-up activities, especially activities 2 and 3.

**Low Achievers:** Provide a glossary and reference material for boldfaced terms in this activity. Organize these students into cooperative learning groups, each of which should include students of higher ability.

## SCORING RUBRIC

Full credit should be given to students who complete the data table and correctly answer all questions, using full sentences. Extra credit should be given for completing follow-up activities.

 **INTERNET TIE-INS**

http://nyelabs.kcts.org/nyeverse/episode/e27.html
http://www.sciencenow.org
http://www.yahoo.com/Scieince/Education/
http://www.mip.berkeley.edu/physics/

 **QUIZ**    In warm climates, many people paint the roofs of their houses white. Why do you think that they do this?

Name_____ Date _____

## ✄ BEFORE YOU BEGIN ✄

In this activity you find out what happens to light when it strikes different surfaces. Surfaces can differ in color, texture, and their ability to transmit light. When light strikes a surface and bounces back, it is called **reflection**. When light strikes a surface and is changed to heat, we say that it is **absorbed**. Some substances are able both to absorb and reflect light at the same time. A substance that light cannot pass through is called **opaque**. When light passes through a substance, we say that the light has been **transmitted**.

If you have ever put your hand near a lightbulb that has been on even for a few seconds, you know that it feels warm. This is because the light energy has been transformed into heat energy. You will apply this concept to explain why different surfaces—for example, surfaces with differences in color, texture, and **opacity**—affect how light is absorbed and reflected. You will determine how these surfaces affect light by noting changes in the temperature of water contained in flasks with different surface characteristics. In this activity, you will shine light on four flasks. Each flask has the same amount of water but different surface characteristics. You will then measure the changes in the temperature of the water in each flask. You will use the changes in water temperature to determine how effective each flask's surface is in the absorption of light.

## MATERIALS

- Lamp with 100-watt light bulb
- Four Erlenmeyer flasks: one black, one white, one silver, and one plain
- Four alcohol thermometers
- Four one-hole stoppers
- Glycerin
- 100-ml graduated cylinder

## PROCEDURE

1. Fill each of the four flasks with 100 ml of water, using the graduated cylinder.

2. Use glycerin to **lubricate** the holes in each of the four one-hole stoppers. Place a thermometer in each stopper, then insert each stopper in a flask.

3. Set the flasks on a table where they are shaded from direct sunlight or other direct sources of light that might raise the water temperature. After 10 minutes, read the temperature of the water in each flask and record it in the data table.

4. Place the four flasks at an equal distance (approximately 25 cm) from a 100-watt light source. Turn the light on, and leave the flasks in place for 15 minutes.

5. After 15 minutes, read the temperature in each flask and record it in the data table.

*(continued)*

## How Do Different Materials Affect the Absorption of Light? *(continued)*

 DATA COLLECTION AND ANALYSIS

### Data Table

| Flask Surface | Initial Water Temp. °C | Final Water Temp. °C | Temperature Change |
|---|---|---|---|
| Clear | | | |
| Silver | | | |
| Black | | | |
| White | | | |

Record your answers on the back of the sheet.

1. Based on the data you have collected, which flask had the greatest increase in water temperature?

2. Which flask had the least change in water temperature?

3. List the four flasks in order, from least to greatest change in temperature.

4. A substance that light cannot pass through is said to be **opaque**. Which flasks are opaque? Which flask is transparent?

5. What factors affected the amount of energy absorbed by each opaque flask?

## ❓ CONCLUDING QUESTIONS

1. Why was it important to place the flasks at equal distances from the light source?

2. Why was an equal amount of water placed in each flask?

3. How did the four flasks differ from one another?

4. Write a paragraph that explains to your classmates what you have learned about how different surfaces affect absorption and reflection of light.

5. People often wear dark clothes in winter and light clothes in summer. Write a paragraph explaining why you think this is done. Support your ideas with appropriate data.

---

### ⚜ FOLLOW-UP ACTIVITIES ⚜

1. Design one additional experiment that you can perform to test a different factor that affects how a substance absorbs light energy.

2. What are some possible sources of error in this experiment?

3. If the black and white flasks had shiny surfaces, the results of this experiment might have been different. How do you think changing the surface texture from dull to shiny would affect the results? Design an experiment that tests this hypothesis.

---

# What Kinds of Images Do Curved Mirrors Produce?

 ## INSTRUCTIONAL OBJECTIVES

Students will be able to

- record observations.
- describe the images formed in concave and convex mirrors.
- locate the focal point of a concave mirror.
- define the terms *concave, convex, converging, diverging, focal point.*
- draw conclusions based on observations.

## NATIONAL SCIENCE STANDARDS ADDRESSED

Students demonstrate understanding of

- the characteristics of images in concave and convex mirrors.
- the relationship between distance from a concave mirror and the reflected image.
- interactions between light and matter.

Students demonstrate scientific inquiry and problem-solving skills by

- using physical science concepts to explain observations.
- identifying a problem and evaluating the outcomes of its investigation.
- working individually and in teams to collect and share information and ideas.

Students demonstrate effective scientific communication by

- arguing from evidence.
- representing data and results in multiple ways.
- explaining scientific concepts to other students.

Students demonstrate competence with the tools and technologies of science by

- using technology and tools.

 ## MATERIALS

- Shaving mirror
- Ray box
- White cardboard
- Convex mirror
- Concave mirror
- Pencil
- Ruler

## HELPFUL HINTS AND DISCUSSION

**Time frame:** Two periods
**Structure:** Individual students or cooperative learning groups
**Location:** In class

Shaving or makeup mirrors that produce an enlarged image are sold in drugstores and variety stores. The mirrors are generally two-sided, one side being a plane mirror and the other an enlarging (curved) mirror. It is important that students understand which side to use. A ray box is used to produce parallel rays of light; it can be purchased commercially or made by the teacher or students. To construct a ray box, use two pieces of wood, approximately 25 cm by 6 cm, held together with crosspieces. The box has no bottom. Mount a double convex lens at the front and cut a groove into the sides, in front of the lens, to hold cards with slits, which are used to produce rays. The light source, which is mounted in a sliding assembly, consists of a 12-volt, 24-watt automobile lamp. The lamp holder has a sleeve of brass tubing that just fits into a hole in the sliding assembly. By moving the sliding assembly, focused parallel rays of light can be obtained. A piece of cardboard can have several slits cut into it to produce parallel rays of light. (See the diagram.) The lamp should be pushed down as far as possible. If you do not have concave and convex mirrors, you can use shiny serving or soupspoons or Mylar™ (available at art supply stores) mounted on cardboard.

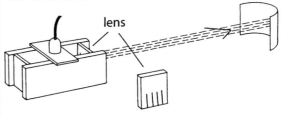

*(continued)*

---

### ADAPTATIONS FOR HIGH AND LOW ACHIEVERS

**High Achievers:** Encourage these students to do the follow-up activities, particularly activities 1 and 3.

**Low Achievers:** Provide a glossary and reference material for boldfaced terms in this activity. Organize these students into cooperative learning groups, each of which should include students of higher ability.

---

### SCORING RUBRIC

Full credit should be given to students who draw required diagrams, record observations, and correctly answer all questions, using full sentences. Extra credit should be given for completing follow-up activities.

---

 **INTERNET TIE-INS**    http://mip.berkeley.edu/physics/E+40+30.html
http://nyelabs.kcts.org/nyeverse
http://odin.phys.bris.ac.uk8080
http://www.sciencenow.org
http://www.nasa.gov

 **QUIZ**    1.  Why are shaving and makeup mirrors concave?
2.  Describe a diverging mirror.
3.  Describe the image reflected by a convex mirror.

# What Kinds of Images Do Curved Mirrors Produce?

✵ BEFORE YOU BEGIN ✵

In this activity you will explore the characteristics of the images formed in curved mirrors. Curved mirrors can curve inward or outward. Mirrors that curve in, with their reflective surfaces inside, are called **concave.** Mirrors that curve out, with their reflective surfaces outside, are called **convex** mirrors.

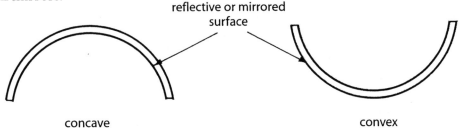

reflective or mirrored
surface

concave                                                              convex

In your investigation of the image formed in a curved mirror, you will want to know how the size of the object in the mirror compares with the size of the original object. You will also want to know if the mirror image is **erect** (right side up) or **inverted** (upside down). Light rays that come together are said to **converge,** and light rays that separate are said to **diverge.** A mirror that causes light rays to come together is called a **converging mirror.** A mirror that causes light rays to spread apart is called a **diverging mirror.** You will determine which mirror, convex or concave, is converging and which is diverging.

 MATERIALS

- Shaving mirror
- Ray box
- Convex mirror
- Concave mirror

- White cardboard
- Pencil
- Ruler

PROCEDURE

Record your observations and answers on the back of the sheet.

1. Hold the shaving mirror no more than 50 cm from your face and look into it. If the mirror has two sides, be sure that you are using the side indicated by your teacher. Describe the image that you see. Note how the size of the reflection compares with the size of your face, which is the object. As you observe the image and compare it with the object, also consider how far your face is from the mirror, whether the mirror image is erect or inverted, and whether it is right-left reversed.

2. Place the mirror on a stand. Contine to look in it, as you move away from it. Move away from the mirror until you observe a change in the image. Describe how the image has changed.

*(continued)*

## What Kinds of Images Do Curved Mirrors Produce? *(continued)*

3. Set up the ray box by inserting the card with several slits in the front slot. Turn on the light, and adjust the sliding light assembly to produce three parallel rays of light. Place a piece of white cardboard on the table in front of the ray box. Place the concave mirror in front of the light rays, 20–25 cm from the box. You will see the rays reflected back toward the light box. Use a pencil to draw the outline of the curved mirror on the cardboard; mark the point in front of the mirror where the reflected rays cross. Do the reflected rays come together or separate? The point where the rays cross is called the **focal point**. Measure the distance from the focal point to the mirror and record it in the Data Collection and Analysis section below.

4. Turn the cardboard over to make a clean surface. Replace the concave mirror with the convex mirror. Aim the parallel rays of light toward the convex mirror. Use a pencil to draw the outline of the curved mirror and trace the three rays of light on the cardboard. Trace both the **incident rays** and the **reflected rays**. The incident rays are those coming from the light source. The reflected rays are those reflected by the mirror. Do the reflected rays come together or separate? Does the image in this convex mirror appear larger or smaller than the actual object?

### DATA COLLECTION AND ANALYSIS

1. (a) How does the size of the image in the shaving mirror compare with the size of the actual object? _____
   (b) Is the image erect or inverted? _____
   (c) Where in the mirror does the image appear? _____
   (d) Is the image right-left reversed? _____

2. What happens to the image when you move away from the mirror? _____
   _____

3. (a) Do the light rays reflected by the concave mirror come together or separate? _____
   (b) What is the distance between the mirror and the focal point? (This distance is called the **focal length** of the concave mirror.) _____

4. (a) Do the rays reflected by the convex mirror come together or separate? _____
   (b) Is the image formed in a convex mirror larger or smaller than the actual object? _____

5. On the back of this sheet. draw a diagram showing parallel rays of light striking a concave mirror.

6. On the back of this sheet, draw a diagram showing parallel rays of light striking a convex mirror.

*(continued)*

# What Kinds of Images Do Curved Mirrors Produce? *(continued)*

## ❓ CONCLUDING QUESTIONS

1. Which of the two mirrors is a converging mirror and which is a diverging mirror?

   _____

   _____

2. Write a paragraph that explains to your classmates how you know which mirror is converging and which is diverging. _____

   _____

   _____

   _____

3. Write a paragraph that explains to your classmates why a converging mirror makes things look larger. (You may want to use a diagram to help explain this **phenomenon**.)

   _____

   _____

   _____

4. Write a paragraph that explains to your classmates why a diverging mirror makes things look smaller. (You may also want to use a diagram to help explain this phenomenon.)

   _____

   _____

   _____

   _____

---

### 🎇 FOLLOW-UP ACTIVITIES 🎇

1. Suggest one additional experiment to investigate how changing the **curvature** of a concave mirror affects its focal length.

2. Investigate how curved mirrors are used in radiotelescopes.

3. Research how concave mirrors are used to focus light in microscopes.

4. Investigate the use of curved mirrors in spotlights.

---

*19*

# How Can We Design and Construct a Fun-House Mirror?

 **INSTRUCTIONAL OBJECTIVES**

Students will be able to

- record observations.
- construct a fun-house mirror by applying scientific principles.
- design a fun-house mirror with specific properties.
- draw conclusions based on observations.

 **NATIONAL SCIENCE STANDARDS ADDRESSED**

Students demonstrate understanding of

- the characteristics of images in concave and convex mirrors.
- interactions between light and matter.

Students demonstrate scientific inquiry and problem-solving skills by

- using physical science concepts to explain observations.
- identifying a problem and evaluating the outcomes of its investigation.
- evaluating designs of fun-house mirrors.
- working in teams to collect and share information and ideas.

 **MATERIALS**

- Sheet of Mylar™
- Sheet of 2- to 4-ply poster board
- Glue stick
- Paper or cloth towel
- Pencil

## HELPFUL HINTS AND DISCUSSION

**Time frame:** One period
**Structure:** Cooperative learning groups of two or more students
**Location:** In class

Mylar can be purchased at an art supply store. It is fragile and flimsy, so it should be glued or taped to a piece of poster board to give it body. Each large Mylar sheet and piece of poster board can be cut in half to supply two cooperative learning groups. Warn students to hold the Mylar by the edges to avoid fingerprints. This activity allows students to apply previously learned scientific concepts to solve a practical problem. It requires at least two students, one to hold the mirror while the other looks into it.

## ADAPTATIONS FOR HIGH AND LOW ACHIEVERS

**High Achievers:** Encourage these students to do the follow-up activities, particularly activities 2 and 3.

**Low Achievers:** Discussing students' experiences in fun houses could be a good way to motivate students for this activity. Before students start on this activity, the teacher should demonstrate how to use and handle Mylar. Organize these students into cooperative learning groups, each of which should include students of higher ability. Provide a glossary and reference for the boldfaced terms in this activity.

## SCORING RUBRIC

Full credit should be given to students who draw required diagrams, record observations, and correctly answer all questions, using full sentences. Extra credit should be given for completing follow-up activities.

 **INTERNET TIE-INS**

http://www.sceincenow.org
http:www.phys.vt.edu/teaching/demos.html
http://nyelabs.kcts.org/

 **QUIZ**

1. Which kind of mirror will make things look larger? Describe it.
2. How does the image in a converging mirror compare with the actual object?

Name_____  Date _____

---

### ✒ BEFORE YOU BEGIN ✒

In this activity, you will apply principles you learned in the activity titled "What Kinds of Images Do Curved Mirrors Produce?" Working as an engineer, you will use what you know about convex and concave mirrors to design and construct a fun-house mirror. You will be working with a sheet of Mylar™. Since it is easy to leave fingerprints on Mylar, try to hold it by the edges.

**MATERIALS**

- Sheet of Mylar
- Glue stick
- Pencil
- Sheet of poster board
- Paper or cloth towel

**PROCEDURE**

1. Follow these instructions to make a flexible mirror. Place the sheet of Mylar on the sheet of poster board and center it. Use a pencil to mark the outline of the Mylar sheet. Apply glue from a glue stick to the poster board, staying within the pencil borders that you marked. Place the Mylar sheet on the center of the poster board. Using a cloth or paper towel, press the Mylar down, working from the center toward the edges so it adheres smoothly to the poster board. Allow time for the glue to dry.

   Record your observations and answers on the back of this sheet.

2. One member of the team should hold and manipulate the flexible mirror. The other person should look into it and make observations for the team.
   (a) While holding the mirror **horizontally**, bend the mirror to make it concave. Describe the image that you observe.
   (b) Increase the **curvature** of the concave mirror and record how this affects the image.
   (c) While holding the mirror **vertically**, bend the mirror to make it concave. Describe the image that you observe.
   (d) While holding the mirror **horizontally**, bend the mirror to make it convex. Describe the image that you observe.
   (e) Increase the curvature of the convex mirror and record how this affects the image.

horizontal—wide mirror

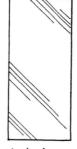
vertical—long mirror

*(continued)*

## How Can We Design and Construct a Fun-House Mirror? *(continued)*

(f) While holding the mirror vertically, bend the mirror to make it convex. Describe the image that you observe in the Data Collection and Analysis section.

 **DATA COLLECTION AND ANALYSIS**

(a) Describe the appearance of your image in the wide concave mirror.

(b) How does increasing the curvature affect the image in the concave mirror?

(c) How does the image in the narrow (vertical) concave mirror compare with the image in the wide (horizontal) concave mirror?

(d) Describe the appearance of your image in the wide convex mirror.

(e) How does increasing the curvature affect the image in the convex mirror?

(f) How does the image in the narrow (vertical) convex mirror compare with the image in the wide (horizontal) convex mirror?

 **CONCLUDING QUESTIONS**

You will now use your observations to design a fun-house mirror. Using the information you have gathered about curved mirrors, you will design a mirror with particular **specifications** and draw a **profile** of that mirror. By *profile,* we mean a drawing that shows the shape of the mirror. For example, a mirror that is made up of a convex mirror on top and a concave mirror on the bottom would have a profile like this:

mirror profile

1. Draw the profile of a mirror that would make your head look thin and your body look fat.

2. Using the flexible mirror, form it into the profile you drew in step 1. See if the mirror you designed does what you expected. Describe your findings.

3. Draw the profile of a mirror that would make your head look thin, your body look fat, and your legs look thin.

4. Using the flexible mirror, form it into the profile you drew in step 3. See if the mirror you designed does what you expected. Describe your findings.

5. Design your own mirror. Decide what you want it to do, draw its profile, and build it.

---

 **FOLLOW-UP ACTIVITIES**

1. Research the work performed by optical engineers.

2. Design an additional fun-house mirror.

3. Research the use of wide-angle mirrors.

4. Research anamorphic art. Locate and demonstrate examples of this kind of art.

# How Is a Shadow Formed?

 ## INSTRUCTIONAL OBJECTIVES

Students will be able to

- record observations.
- explain the formation of a shadow.
- distinguish between the umbra and the penumbra.
- draw conclusions based on observations.

 ## NATIONAL SCIENCE STANDARDS ADDRESSED

Students demonstrate understanding of

- the characteristics of shadows.
- interactions between light and matter.

Students demonstrate scientific inquiry and problem-solving skills by

- using physical science concepts to explain observations.
- identifying a problem and evaluating the outcomes of its investigation.
- working in teams to collect and share information and ideas.

Students demonstrate effective scientific communication by

- arguing from evidence.
- explaining scientific concepts to other students.

Students demonstrate competence with the tools and technologies of science by

- using laboratory equipment and tools.
- using a graph to analyze data.

## MATERIALS

- Flashlight
- Meterstick
- Rubber ball
- Glass plate
- Piece of plastic
- Small opaque pill bottle (5–8 cm high)
- Table

### HELPFUL HINTS AND DISCUSSION

**Time frame:** One or two periods
**Structure:** Cooperative learning groups of two or more students
**Location:** In class or at home

This activity works best with a light source that is focused and directional—a flashlight works well. Since the light source and the object must be held while measurements are taken, each cooperative learning group needs a minimum of two students.

### ADAPTATIONS FOR HIGH AND LOW ACHIEVERS

**High Achievers:** Ask these students to derive additional information from graphed data and to explain why graphing data is useful. Also, encourage these students to perform the follow-up activities, particularly activities 2 and 3.

**Low Achievers:** Provide a glossary and reference material for bold-faced terms in this activity. Demonstrate the setup for procedure 3 before students start working on it. Also, review how to enter data in the data table and how to graph it. Students with weak math backgrounds may need a lesson on graphing. Organize these students into cooperative learning groups, each of which should include students of higher ability.

### SCORING RUBRIC

Full credit should be given to students who record observations and answer all questions correctly, using full sentences. Extra credit should be given for completing follow-up activities.

*(continued)*

 **INTERNET TIE-INS**    http://www.exploratorium.edu/
http://nyelabs.kcts.org/nyeverse/
http://www.sciencenow.org
http://www.yahoo.com.Science/Education/

 **QUIZ**    1. As indicated in the diagram below, two lights of the same wattage are set up facing a screen. An opaque object is placed one meter from the first light and an identical object is placed three meters from the second light. Which object will form the larger shadow on the screen? Explain why.

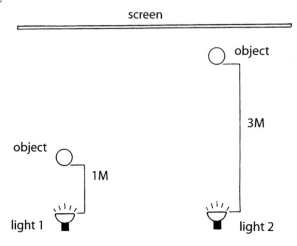

2. How does the penumbra of a shadow differ from the umbra ?

# How Is a Shadow Formed?

### ✂ BEFORE YOU BEGIN ✂

Have you ever held your hand in front of a light to make a shadow, perhaps to make shadows that look like different animals? Today you are going to learn more about the nature of shadows and how they are formed. Distances are very important when you investigate shadows, especially the distance between the light source (like a flashlight) and the object, and the distance between the light source (flashlight) and the shadow. If you look at many shadows, you will observe a darker part called the **umbra** and a lighter part called the **penumbra.**

## MATERIALS

- Flashlight
- Rubber ball
- Piece of plastic
- Table

- Meterstick
- Glass plate
- Small opaque pill bottle (5–8 cm high)

## PROCEDURE

Record your observations, answers, and drawings on the back of this sheet.

1  (a) Position a flashlight on a table in a darkened room so that it is directed toward a white wall at a distance of 40 cm. Turn on the flashlight and place the following objects approximately 15 cm in front of the light, one at a time: rubber ball, glass plate, piece of translucent plastic, your hand, and small opaque pill bottle. In the Data Collection and Analysis section, record which objects form shadows.

   (b) In general, what kinds of objects form shadows? Test your generalization by placing other objects in front of the flashlight. Add these observations to those you have already entered in the table in the Data Collection section.

2. Hold the flashlight approximately 35 cm from a white wall or screen and turn it on. Now, place your finger approximately 10 cm in front of the light. In the Data Collection section, draw the shadow as it appears. Label the umbra and penumbra.

3. Place the flashlight approximately 50 cm from the wall on a flat surface, such as a table, that is adjacent to the wall. Position a meterstick next to the flashlight, parallel to the light beam, so that it extends to the wall and the lens of the flashlight is at the 50-cm mark. Place the pill bottle at the 45-cm mark and measure the height of the shadow created. Record this information in the data table. Move the pill bottle to the 40-cm mark, and again measure the height of its shadow. Record this information in the data table.

*(continued)*

## How Is a Shadow Formed? *(continued)*

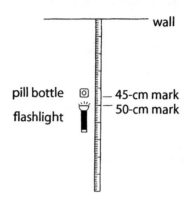

wall

pill bottle — 45-cm mark

flashlight — 50-cm mark

4. Repeat procedure 3 with the pill bottle located at the 35-cm, 30-cm, 25-cm, and 20-cm marks.

 **DATA COLLECTION AND ANALYSIS**

1. (a) For each object you tested, indicate whether a shadow forms; describe the shadow if one forms.

| Object | Forms a Shadow (Y or N) | Description of Shadow (fuzzy or sharp) |
|---|---|---|
| Rubber ball | | |
| Glass plate | | |
| Translucent plastic | | |
| Your hand | | |
| Pill bottle | | |

1. (b) Make a generalization about the nature of objects that create shadows.

2. Draw the shadow formed by your finger and label the umbra and penumbra.

3. Record the data that you collect during procedures 3 and 4.

| Distance Between Light and Object (cm) | Distance Between Light and Wall (cm) | Height of Shadow (cm) |
|---|---|---|
| 5 cm | 50 cm | |
| 10 cm | 50 cm | |
| 15 cm | 50 cm | |
| 20 cm | 50 cm | |
| 25 cm | 50 cm | |

*(continued)*

## How is a Shadow Formed? *(continued)*

 CONCLUDING QUESTIONS

1. Write a statement that summarizes what you have learned about objects that form shadows.

2. Plot the data from the data table on the graph below.

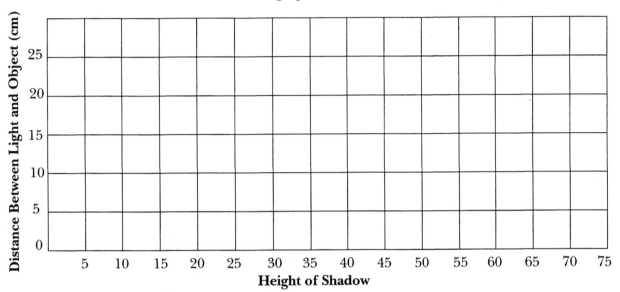

(Note: The distance between light and shadow is constant.)

3. Write a sentence describing the relationship between the distance of an object from a light source and the size of the shadow formed.

---

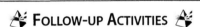 FOLLOW-UP ACTIVITIES

1. Research the lunar eclipse. Apply what you have learned about shadows to explain this phenomenon.

2. Explain the difference between a partial and a full solar eclipse.

3. Your school would like to perform a shadow play using finger shadows. Determine where the projector, the screen, and the performer must be located to create shadows large enough to be seen on a 10-foot screen. Explain how you determined this.

4. Compare and contrast the shadow formed by light from a point source with the shadow formed by light from an **extended light source.**

5. Look up the formation of shadows in your textbook and write an explanation of why the umbra and penumbra form. You may use a diagram to help explain this phenomenon.

---

# How Can We Make a Pinhole Camera?

 **INSTRUCTIONAL OBJECTIVES**

Students will be able to

- record observations.
- explain formation of an image by a pinhole camera.
- construct a pinhole camera.
- draw conclusions based on observations.

 **NATIONAL SCIENCE STANDARDS ADDRESSED**

Students demonstrate understanding of

- the pinhole camera.
- interactions between light and matter.

Students demonstrate scientific inquiry and problem-solving skills by

- using physical science concepts to explain observations.
- identifying a problem and evaluating the outcomes of its investigation.
- working individually and in teams to collect and share information and ideas.

Students demonstrate effective scientific communication by

- arguing from evidence.
- explaining scientific concepts to other students.

Students demonstrate competence with the tools and technologies of science by

- constructing a pinhole camera.

 **MATERIALS**

- Cardboard box
- Scissors
- Tissue paper
- Masking tape
- Straight pin
- Pencil
- Piece of aluminum foil
- Lamp with candelabra bulb
- Dark cloth or bath towel (optional)

## HELPFUL HINTS AND DISCUSSION

**Time frame:** Two periods
**Structure:** Individual students or cooperative learning groups
**Location:** In class or at home

A variety of cardboard boxes may be used to make the camera—shoe box, cereal box, or tissue box. Any holes in the box should be covered with masking tape to prevent light leaks. Tissue paper may be replaced with wax paper or lens paper. A candelabra bulb is suggested because its shape makes it easier for students to see that the image is inverted. The cloth or towel reduces extraneous light that may interfere with seeing the image. Some students may need help locating the image the first time.

## ADAPTATIONS FOR HIGH AND LOW ACHIEVERS

**High Achievers:** Encourage these students to do the follow-up activities, particularly activities 2 and 3.
**Low Achievers:** Constructing the pinhole camera should be supervised by the teacher or a parent. Procedures 5 and 6 should be done with adult supervision. The teacher should review the data table with these students and explain the type of data expected.

## SCORING RUBRIC

Full credit should be given to students who record observations and answer all questions correctly, using full sentences. Extra credit should be given for completing follow-up activities.

 **INTERNET TIE-INS**   hhttp://www.yahoo.com/science/education/
hhttp://www.mos.org/
http:www.astro.uiuc.edu/~pmcc/comet/pinhole.html
http://interact.uoregon.edu/MedialLit/FA/MLCurriculum/pinhole.html

 **QUIZ**   How does increasing the size of the pinhole in a pinhole camera affect the image?

# How Can We Make a Pinhole Camera?

---

### ✤ BEFORE YOU BEGIN ✤

In this activity, you will construct a pinhole camera and explore the properties of the image that it forms. In the process, you will learn more about the nature of light.

## MATERIALS

- Cardboard box
- Tissue paper
- Straight pin
- Piece of aluminum foil
- Dark cloth or bath towel (optional)

- Scissors
- Masking tape
- Pencil
- Lamp with candelabra bulb

## PROCEDURE

Record your observations and answers on the back of this sheet. Carry out all procedures during daylight hours, not at night.

1. Cut out a square hole approximately 5 cm × 5 cm in one end of your cardboard box.

2. Cut a piece of the tissue paper into a square, approximately 6 cm.

3. Tape the tissue paper over the square cutout in the box. The tissue paper will serve as a translucent screen that allows you to see the image.

4. At the opposite end of the box, mark the point that is in line with the center of the 5 cm × 5 cm square cutout. Place a small piece of masking tape over this point and make a small hole in it with a straight pin. This is the **pinhole**.

5. With the pinhole facing the lamp with the candelabra lightbulb, hold the box so the tissue paper screen is approximately 20 cm from your face. Observe the image of the lightbulb on the screen. If you do not see the image, move the camera until you do. The image will appear on the screen, not inside the box. Describe the image you see. Try moving the camera closer and farther from the lightbulb, and observe how changing the distance affects the size of the image.

6. Hold the camera with the pinhole toward a window in the room, and describe the image you see. If you have difficulty seeing an image, try putting a dark cloth or towel over your head and the back of the camera to reduce excess light.

7. Using a pencil point, double the size of the pinhole and repeat your observations of the light-bulb and window. Describe how increasing the size of the pinhole affects the image.

8. Using the point of the scissors, double the size of the pinhole again and repeat your observations of both the lightbulb and window. Once again, describe how increasing the size of the pinhole affects the image.

*(continued)*

## How Can We Make a Pinhole Camera? *(continued)*

9. Tape a piece of aluminum foil over the hole. Using a straight pin, make two pinholes in the center of the foil where it covers the enlarged hole in the cardboard. Repeat your observations of the lightbulb and window and record your observations.

 DATA COLLECTION AND ANALYSIS

1. Describe the image of the candelabra lightbulb that you see. Draw the image that you see.

2. How does changing the distance between the object (lightbulb) and the camera affect the size of the image?

3. Describe the image you see when the camera is pointed toward the window.

4. Describe the images you see with two pinholes in the aluminum foil.

5. Complete the table below to compare your observations of the brightness and sharpness of images formed with different-sized pinholes.

| Size of Pinhole | Brightness | Sharpness |
|---|---|---|
| 1. Made with pin | | |
| 2. Made with pencil point (size of original hole doubled) | | |
| 3. Made with scissors point (size of original hole quadrupled) | | |

## CONCLUDING QUESTIONS

1. Based on your observations, what are the characteristics of an image formed by a pinhole camera?

   _____

   _____

   _____

2. Based on your observations, how does the size of the pinhole affect the image formed?

   _____

   _____

   _____

*(continued)*

## How Can We Make a Pinhole Camera? *(continued)*

3. What factors affect the image formed by a pinhole camera?

_____

_____

_____

4. How can a pinhole camera be used to show that light travels in straight lines?

_____

_____

_____

5. How can a pinhole camera be used to observe a solar eclipse?

_____

_____

_____

---

### 🔦 FOLLOW-UP ACTIVITIES 🔦

1. A pinhole camera like the one you built can be combined with a film cartridge to take real photographs. The diagram below shows how to do it. Build a camera and take some photographs. Experiment with different objects and different exposure times. You can use a coin to advance the film.

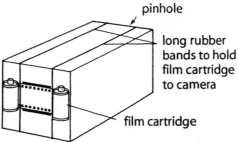

pinhole

long rubber bands to hold film cartridge to camera

film cartridge

2. Another method of taking photographs with a pinhole camera is to use a camera with a removable lens. Remove the lens and cover the opening with a piece of aluminum foil. Make a pinhole in the aluminum foil and take pictures.

3. Research the history of the *camera obscura.*

4. Research use of the pinhole camera to take photographs of stars and comets.

**INSTRUCTIONAL OBJECTIVES**

Students will be able to

- record observations.
- state the law of refraction (Snell's law).
- determine if light is refracted when it passes from one medium to another.
- predict the direction in which light will be refracted.
- define the terms *refraction, medium, index of refraction, oblique.*
- draw conclusions based on observations.

 **NATIONAL SCIENCE STANDARDS ADDRESSED**

Students demonstrate understanding of

- the law of refraction.
- interactions between light and matter.

Students demonstrate scientific inquiry and problem-solving skills by

- using physical science concepts to explain observations.
- identifying a problem and evaluating the outcomes of its investigation.
- working individually and in teams to collect and share information and ideas.

Students demonstrate effective scientific communication by

- arguing from evidence.
- explaining scientific concepts to other students.

Students demonstrate competence with the tools and technologies of science by

- using a protractor and ruler.

**MATERIALS**

- Narrow-beam light source
- Block of clear plastic, such as Lucite™ or Plexiglas™, approx. 18 cm × 4 cm
- Block of glass, approx. 18 cm × 4 cm
- Four sheets of white paper
- Protractor
- Pencil
- Ruler

---

**HELPFUL HINTS AND DISCUSSION**

**Time frame:** One or two periods
**Structure:** Individual students or cooperative learning groups
**Location:** In class or at home

To do this activity, students need a light source with a narrow beam. Light boxes and ray projectors can be purchased from various commercial supply houses, or you can use the ray box described in the activity titled "What Kinds of Images Do Curved Mirrors Produce?" You can make a light source from a flashlight. Over the flashlight lens, tape a piece of cardboard cut to the size and shape of the flashlight lens, with a hole about the size of a hole-punch in its center. (Note: Indices of refraction for glass and plastics vary, depending on the specific glass or plastic.)

---

**ADAPTATIONS FOR HIGH AND LOW ACHIEVERS**

**High Achievers:** Introduce the term *interface* in discussing refraction with this group. Encourage these students to do the follow-up activities, particularly activities 1 and 3.

**Low Achievers:** Provide a glossary and reference material for bold-faced terms in this activity. Review the data table with these students. Also, demonstrate how to use a protractor and verify that students can use one. Have students carry out this activity in class supervised by a teacher who can help them. The teacher should use a blackboard optics kit to demonstrate this activity before students attempt it.

---

**SCORING RUBRIC**

Full credit should be given to students who record observations and answer all questions correctly, using full sentences. Extra credit should be given for completing follow-up activities.

*(continued)*

 **INTERNET TIE-INS**

hhtp://www.yahoo.com/Science/Education/
hhtp://wwwmos.org/
hhtp://www.cbu.edu/~jvarrian/snellcai.html
hhtp:www.sasked.gov.sk.ca/physics/u3c12phy.html

 **QUIZ**

1. A beam of light passes at a 30° angle from air to water. What will happen to the direction of the beam of light in the water?

2. A beam of light passes from water to glass at a 90° angle. Describe the path of this beam of light.

# What Happens When Light Passes into a New Medium?

### 🎁 BEFORE YOU BEGIN 🎁

Have you ever dropped a coin in a swimming pool and tried to pick it up? You may have found that the coin was not where it seemed to be. In this activity you explore the reasons for this and similar occurrences. Light does not travel through all **media** at the same speed. It travels fastest through a **vacuum** and more slowly through other media. The **index of refraction** of a substance is a calculation based on how fast light travels through it. For example, the index of refraction for a vacuum is 1 and the index of refraction for water, in which light travels more slowly, is 1.3. The higher the index of refraction, the slower the light travels through something. **Note:** You should carry out this activity in a darkened room to make it easier to observe the beam of light.

##  MATERIALS

- Narrow-beam light source
- Block of clear plastic, such as Lucite™ or Plexiglas™, approx. 18 cm × 4 cm
- Block of glass, approx. 18 cm × 4 cm

- Four sheets of white paper
- Protractor
- Pencil
- Ruler

##  PROCEDURE

Record your observations in the table in the Data Collection and Analysis section.

1. Place the block of plastic on a sheet of white paper and trace its outline. Use a protractor to draw a line that is **perpendicular** to the outline of the block of plastic. Label this line the **normal**. Remove the plastic block and extend this line inside the outline.

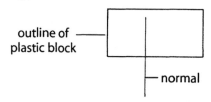

2. Replace the block of plastic on top of the outline. Shine the beam of light along the normal. Do you see any changes in the path that the light ray follows?

3. Remove the block and draw a line that forms a 30° angle with the normal. This angle is called the **angle of incidence**, and the line is called the **incident ray.**

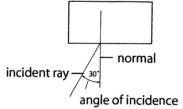

*(continued)*

## What Happens When Light Passes into a New Medium? *(continued)*

4. Replace the block. Shine the beam of light along the incident ray. Observe the ray of light in the block of plastic. Does the ray of light bend inside the block? In which direction? (You may want to use the protractor when you are making these observations.)

5. Note the point where the ray of light leaves the block. Mark this point with a pencil. Remove the block and use the protractor and ruler to draw a normal at this point, extending beyond the outline.

6. Replace the block. Shine the beam of light along the original incident ray. Observe the ray of light leaving the block of plastic. As the ray of light leaves the block, does it bend? in which direction? Repeat step 3–6 using an angle of incidence of 15°.

7. Repeat steps 3–6 using a block of glass in place of the plastic.

### DATA COLLECTION AND ANALYSIS

| Angle of Incidence | Media (from → to) | Observation (did not bend) (bends toward normal) (bends away from normal) |
|---|---|---|
| 90° | air to plastic | |
| 30° | air to plastic | |
| 30° | plastic to air | |
| 15° | air to plastic | |
| 15° | plastic to air | |
| 30° | air to glass | |
| 30° | glass to air | |
| 15° | air to glass | |
| 15° | glass to air | |

### CONCLUDING QUESTIONS

1. Does light bend when it moves from one medium to another at right angles? If so, at what angles?

   _____

   _____

2. Does light bend when it moves from one medium to another at an angle that is less than 90°? If so, at what angles?

   _____

   _____

*(continued)*

## What Happens When Light Passes into a New Medium? *(continued)*

3. In which direction (toward or away from the normal) does light bend when it passes **obliquely** from a medium with a lower index of refraction to a medium with a higher index of refraction?

_____

4. In which direction (toward or away from the normal) does light bend when it passes obliquely from a medium with a higher index of refraction to a medium with a lower index of refraction?

_____

5. Look up the law of refraction in a textbook. Does your data support the law? Explain your answer.

_____

_____

_____

6. Write a brief explanation for your class of what you have learned about the law of refraction.

_____

_____

_____

7. Based on your observations and what you read in the textbook, write a brief explanation of why light bends when it passes obliquely from one medium to another.

_____

_____

_____

_____

---

### ⚜ FOLLOW-UP ACTIVITIES ⚜

1. Design an experiment to test the relative indices of refraction for a variety of transparent liquids—for example, alcohol, oil, Karo syrup, sucrose. The liquids can be placed in Plexiglas cubes for the test.

2. Design an experiment to test the relative indices of refraction for several transparent solids such as various samples of plastic and glass—Plexiglas, Lucite, leaded glass, etc.

3. Design an experiment to investigate the effect on the concentration of sugar in a sugar solution on the solution's index of refraction.

4. Research the causes of mirages.

# What Is Total Internal Reflection?

## ☑ INSTRUCTIONAL OBJECTIVES

Students will be able to

- record observations.
- explain total internal reflection.
- demonstrate total internal reflection.
- define the term *critical angle*.
- draw conclusions based on observations.

##  NATIONAL SCIENCE STANDARDS ADDRESSED

Students demonstrate understanding of

- total internal reflection.
- interactions between light and matter.

Students demonstrate scientific inquiry and problem-solving skills by

- using physical science concepts to explain observations.
- identifying a problem and evaluating the outcomes of its investigation.
- working individually and in teams to collect and share information.

Students demonstrate effective scientific communication by

- arguing from evidence.
- explaining scientific concepts to other students.

Students demonstrate competence with the tools and technologies of science by

- using laboratory equipment.

##  MATERIALS

- Narrow-beam light source
- Block of clear plastic, such as Lucite or Plexiglas
- Block of glass
- Sheets of white paper
- Protractor
- Pencil
- Ruler

## HELPFUL HINTS AND DISCUSSION

**Time frame:** One period
**Structure:** Individual students or cooperative learning groups
**Location:** In class

To do this activity students need a light source with a narrow beam. Light boxes and ray projectors can be purchased from various commercial supply houses or can be made. You can make a light source from a flashlight. Over the flashlight lens, tape a piece of cardboard cut to the shape and size of the flashlight lens, with a hole about the size of a hole punch in the center. (Note: The critical angles for glass and plastics vary, depending on the specific glass or plastic.)

## ADAPTATIONS FOR HIGH AND LOW ACHIEVERS

**High Achievers:** Encourage these students to perform the follow-up activities, particularly activities 1 and 3.

**Low Achievers:** Provide a glossary and reference material for boldfaced terms in this activity. Review how to use a protractor. Have students carry out this activity in class supervised by a teacher who can help them. The teacher should use a blackboard optics kit to demonstrate this activity before students attempt it.

## SCORING RUBRIC

Full credit should be given to students who record observations and answer all questions correctly, using full sentences. Extra credit should be given for completing follow-up activities.

##  INTERNET TIE-INS

hhttp://www.yahoo.com/Science/Education/
hhttp://wwwmos.org/
hhttp://www.cbu.edu/~jvarrian/snellcai.html

##  QUIZ

A ray of light enters a medium from air at an angle that is greater than the critical angle for that medium. What do you expect to observe?

# What Is Total Internal Reflection?

 **BEFORE YOU BEGIN**

Have you ever seen a diamond? If you have, you know that diamonds and other gems sparkle. Gemstones, including diamonds, sparkle because the way that they are cut causes them to reflect light. In this activity, you will explore **total internal reflection**, which is what makes the gemstones sparkle. **Note:** You should carry out this activity in a darkened room to make it easier to observe the beam of light.

##  MATERIALS

- Narrow-beam light source
- Block of clear plastic
- Block of glass
- Sheets of white paper

- Protractor
- Pencil
- Ruler

## PROCEDURE

Record your observations in the table in the Data Collection and Analysis section.

1. Place the block of plastic on a sheet of white paper and trace its outline. Use a protractor to draw a line that is **perpendicular** to the outline of the block of plastic. Label this line the **normal**. Remove the block and extend the normal line inside the outline. Replace the block. Shine the beam of light so that it forms a 15° angle of incidence. What do you observe?

2. Gradually increase the angle of incidence until the light beam does not exit the block but is reflected back into the block. This phenomenon is called **total internal reflection**.

3. Measure the angle at which total internal reflection occurred. This is called the **critical angle**.

4. Increase the angle of incidence and observe what happens.

5. Repeat steps 1–3 with a glass block. What is the critical angle for glass? How does it compare with the critical angle for plastic?

## DATA COLLECTION AND ANALYSIS

1. What is the critical angle for plastic in air?

2. What happens if the angle of incidence is increased beyond the critical angle?

3. Draw a diagram to show total internal reflection.

4. What is the critical angle for glass in air?

*(continued)*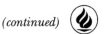

## What Is Total Internal Reflection? *(continued)*

### ❓ CONCLUDING QUESTIONS

1. For your classmates, write a brief explanation of what you have learned about total internal reflection and gemstones.

   _____

   _____

   _____

   _____

2. Using what you have learned about total internal reflection, explain the importance of the angles at which a gemstone is cut.

   _____

   _____

   _____

   _____

3. What factors affect the critical angle?

   _____

   _____

   _____

   _____

---

### ⚗ FOLLOW-UP ACTIVITIES ⚗

1. Research fiber optics and explain how this is an application of total internal reflection.

2. Research the uses of fiber-optic cables.

3. If the block were placed in water, what would you expect to happen to the critical angle? Justify your answer.

---

# How Does Distance Affect the Spread of a Light Spot?

 ## INSTRUCTIONAL OBJECTIVES

Students will be able to

- record observations.
- explain the relationship between the distance of a light source from a screen and the diameter (spread) of a light spot.
- use graphs to interpolate and extrapolate.
- draw conclusions based on observations.

## NATIONAL SCIENCE STANDARDS ADDRESSED

Students demonstrate understanding of

- the relationship between the distance of a light source from a screen and the diameter (spread) of its light spot.
- interactions between light and matter.

Students demonstrate scientific inquiry and problem-solving skills by

- using physical science concepts to explain observations.
- identifying a problem and evaluating the outcomes of its investigation.
- working in teams to collect and share information and ideas.

Students demonstrate effective scientific communication by

- arguing from evidence.
- explaining scientific concepts to other students.

Students demonstrate competence with the tools and technologies of science by

- making measurements.
- using a graph to analyze data.
- acquiring information from a graph by interpolating and extrapolating.

 ## MATERIALS

- Flashlight
- Meterstick
- Blank wall, ceiling, or screen

## HELPFUL HINTS AND DISCUSSION

**Time frame:** Two periods
**Structure:** Cooperative learning groups of two or more students
**Location:** In class or at home

This activity is most successful with a light source that is focused and directional—a flashlight works well. Since the light source and object must be both held while measurements are taken, at least two students must work together on the activity.

## ADAPTATIONS FOR HIGH AND LOW ACHIEVERS

**High Achievers:** Explain plotting an independent variable on the *x*-axis and plotting a dependent variable on the *y*-axis. Introduce the terms *interpolation* and *extrapolation,* as well as the process. Encourage these students to perform the follow-up activities, particularly activities 2 and 4.

**Low Achievers:** Provide a glossary and reference material for boldfaced terms in this activity. Review entering data in a table and graphing data. It may be necessary also to review how to measure diameter. Carefully guide students through interpolation and extrapolation, but do not introduce these terms.

## SCORING RUBRIC

Full credit should be given to students who record observations, complete the data table, correctly graph data, and answer all questions correctly, using full sentences. Extra credit should be given for completing follow-up activities.

*(continued)*

 **INTERNET TIE-INS**    http:www.yahoo.com.Science/Education/
http://www.coseti.org/
http://www.desisti.it/leoftusa.html
http://www.exploratorium.edu.

 **QUIZ**    1.  How does the diameter of a light beam change the farther it is from the light source?
2.  Based on the graph below, what is the diameter of a light beam 8 cm away from a screen?

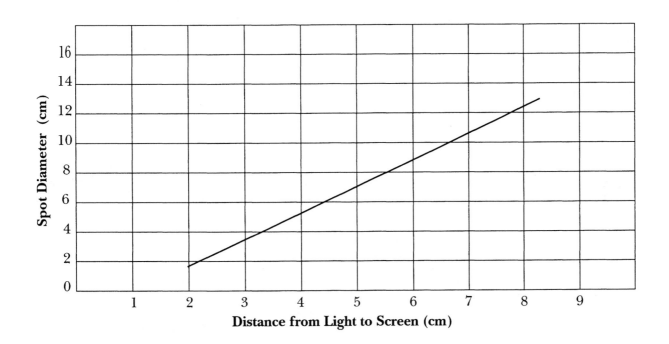

# How Does Distance Affect the Spread of a Light Spot?

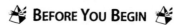 **BEFORE YOU BEGIN**

Have you ever noticed a spotlight in a theater or at a concert? The size of the area that is **illuminated** by the spotlight depends on several factors, including its distance from the stage. In this activity, you will investigate the relationship between the distance of a light source (in this case a flashlight) from the screen it shines on and the **diameter** of the spot of light it produces.

## MATERIALS

- Flashlight
- Blank wall, ceiling, or screen
- Meterstick

 ## PROCEDURE

1. In a darkened room, hold the flashlight 3 cm from a white wall or screen and turn it on. You will see a circle of light, which is the **light spot**. Have your partner measure the diameter of the spot. Enter this measurement in the data table.

2. Repeat step 1 with the flashlight held at distances of 5 cm, 7 cm, 10 cm, 12 cm, and 15 cm. Enter these measurements in the data table below.

3. How does the sharpness of the light spot change as you increase and decrease the distance between the flashlight and the wall?

_____

_____

_____

## DATA COLLECTION AND ANALYSIS

### Data Table

| Distance Between Flashlight and Wall (cm) | Diameter of Light Spot (cm) |
|---|---|
| 3 cm | |
| 5 cm | |
| 7 cm | |
| 10 cm | |
| 12 cm | |
| 15 cm | |

*(continued)*

## How Does Distance Affect the Spread of a Light Spot? *(continued)*

### ❓ CONCLUDING QUESTIONS

1. Based on your observations, what is the relationship between a light source's distance from a screen and the diameter of the light spot it produces?

2. Plot the data from the table on the graph, and circle each point on the graph. After you have plotted all points, draw a solid line to connect them.

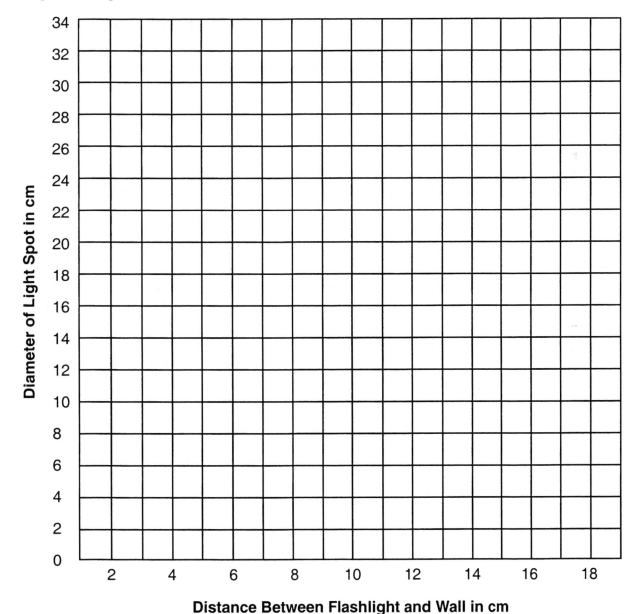

**Diameter of Light Spot in cm** (y-axis: 0, 2, 4, 6, 8, 10, 12, 14, 16, 18, 20, 22, 24, 26, 28, 30, 32, 34)

**Distance Between Flashlight and Wall in cm** (x-axis: 2, 4, 6, 8, 10, 12, 14, 16, 18)

*(continued)*

## How Does Distance Affect the Spread of a Light Spot? *(continued)*

3. Using dotted lines, **extend** the line graph in both directions.

4. Using the graph to estimate values between measured points, locate the light-spot diameters on the graph for distances of 6 cm, 8 cm, and 14 cm. Enter these values in the table below. Repeat step 1 using these distances. Enter the values you measured in the table below. Do the measured values and the values estimated from the graph agree?

5. Using the graph to estimate values beyond the measured points, locate the light-spot diameters on the graph for distances of 2 cm and 16 cm. Enter these values in the table below. Repeat step 1 using these distances. Enter the values you measured in the table below. Do the measured values and the values estimated from the graph agree?

| Distance Between Flashlight and Wall (cm) | Diameter Determined from Graph (cm) | Measured Diameter (cm) |
|---|---|---|
| 2 cm | | |
| 6 cm | | |
| 8 cm | | |
| 14 cm | | |
| 16 cm | | |

Record your answers to the following questions on the back of this sheet.

6. How did the measurements that you made compare to the values you estimated from the graph?

7. You would like to buy a lamp that will illuminate only the work area of your desk. Would it be better to purchase a lamp that stands on your desk or a lamp that hangs from the ceiling over the desk? Explain your answer.

8. Your teacher is planning to use a projector to show slides. The projector is producing a very small image. What should your teacher do to increase the size of the image? Explain your answer.

---

### ✄ FOLLOW-UP ACTIVITIES ✄

1. Use your graph to determine the light-spot diameter that you would expect at distances from the wall of 1 cm, 4 cm, and 11 cm.

2. Propose an experiment to determine how distance affects the sharpness of a light beam.

3. Research how distance is used to control the spread of the light beam for theatrical spotlights.

4. Research the importance of beam spreading in astronomical research.

---

# How Do Chemicals Produce Light?

## ✓ INSTRUCTIONAL OBJECTIVES

Students will be able to

- record observations.
- define the term *chemiluminescence.*
- draw conclusions based on observations.
- explain the importance of controlling variables in an experiment.

## 🌐 NATIONAL SCIENCE STANDARDS ADDRESSED

Students demonstrate understanding of

- chemiluminescence.
- interactions between light and chemical energy.

Students demonstrate scientific inquiry and problem-solving skills by

- using physical science concepts to explain observations.
- identifying a problem and evaluating the outcome of its investigation.
- working individually and in teams to collect and share information and ideas.
- identifying and controlling experimental variables.

Students demonstrate effective scientific communication by

- arguing from evidence.
- explaining scientific concepts to other students.

Students demonstrate competence with the tools and technologies of science by

- using a thermometer.
- using a graduated cylinder.

##  MATERIALS

- Three light sticks
- Three 400-ml beakers
- Thermometer
- Water at room temperature
- Ice water
- Hot water (60°–70° C)
- 500-ml graduated cylinder

## HELPFUL HINTS AND DISCUSSION

**Time frame:** One period
**Structure:** Individual students or cooperative learning groups
**Location:** In class

Light sticks are available from chemical supply houses, as well as at some camping supply and sporting goods stores. They are perfectly safe to use and can be disposed of with ordinary trash. Allow students to take the light sticks home for further investigation, but warn them not to break or puncture them, since the chemicals they contain will stain clothes. A light stick consists of several chemicals in a thin glass ampule surrounded by other chemicals, all contained within a flexible plastic tube. When the tube is bent the ampule breaks and releases its contents, which mix with the chemicals in the outer layer. Light sticks should be stored in their foil wrappers until ready for use.

To spark enthusiam for this activity, you can demonstrate chemiluminescence. A dramatic example is the oxidation of luminol. In this demonstration, you pour a colorless liquid and a blue liquid simultaneously into a glass funnel attached to a spiral delivery tube that empties into a beaker. The mixed liquids emit a blue light through the tube. (Conduct this demonstration in a darkened room for maximum effect.) Here is how to prepare the the two solutions.

### Solution A

In a 1-liter flask, dissolve 4 g of sodium carbonate in 500 ml of distilled water. Add 0.2 g luminol and stir to dissolve. Add 24 g of sodium bicarbonate, 0.5 g ammonium carbonate monohydrate, and 0.4 g copper(II)sulfate penthydrate, and stir to dissolve. Dilute this solution to 1 liter.

### Solution B

Dilute 50 ml of 3% hydrogen peroxide to 1 liter with distilled water.

*(continued)*

<table>
<tr><td>

**ADAPTATIONS FOR HIGH AND LOW ACHIEVERS**

**High Achievers:** Discuss the design of this experiment and empha-size the importance of controlling variables. Review the definitions of *control,* as well as *independent* and *dependent variables.* Encourage these students to do the follow-up activities, particularly activities 2 and 3.

**Low Achievers:** Provide a glossary and reference material for bold-faced terms in this activity. Organize these students into cooperative learning groups, each of which should include students of higher abiliby. Discuss designing experiments and explain the importance of controlling variables. Elicit the reason for immersing all three light sticks in the beakers of water at the temperatures suggested.

</td><td>

**SCORING RUBRIC**

Full credit should be given to students who record observations and correctly answer all questions, using full sentences. Extra credit should be given for completing follow-up activities.

</td></tr>
</table>

 **INTERNET TIE-INS**    hhtp://www.yahoo.com/Science/Education/
hhtp://www.mos.org/
http://scifun.chem.wise.edu/HOMEEXPTS/chemilum.html
http://chemed.chem.purdue.edu/

 **QUIZ**    1.  Describe the phenomenon of chemiluminescence and explain how it occurs.
2.  What is meant by the term "cool light"?

# How Do Chemicals Produce Light?

---

### ✦ BEFORE YOU BEGIN ✦

Energy can be changed from one form to another. For example, when a piece of paper or wood burns, chemical energy is changed into two other forms of energy: light and heat. Some chemical reactions release light at room temperature. We call light produced without heat "cool light." You may have seen examples of such "cool light" at a circus or carnival, where light tubes are sold which you could wear as bracelets or necklaces. The process by which chemical energy is released as "cool light" is called **chemiluminescence**. In this activity you will investigate this phenomenon.

---

 ## MATERIALS

- Three light sticks
- Three 400-ml beakers
- Thermometer
- Water at room temperature

- Ice water
- Hot water (approximately 60°–70° C)
- 500-ml graduated cylinder

## PROCEDURE

Record your answers to questions on the back of this sheet. Carry out all of the procedures in a darkened room.

1. Measure the air temperature in the room with the thermometer. Use the graduated cylinder to measure 250 ml of water at room temperature. Pour the water into one of the beakers. Use the thermometer to check the temperature of the water in the beaker. If it is not at room temperature, let it sit for several minutes. Remove the wrapper from the first light stick and bend it enough to break the vial inside. Shake the light stick to mix its contents, and observe the reaction. In the Data Collection and Analysis section, describe the appearance of the light stick. What color of light does it emit? Does the entire stick glow, or just the chemicals inside? When the water has reached room temperature, put the light stick in the beaker. Leave the light stick in the beaker of water for five minutes. Use the thermometer to determine the temperature of the water. Has the water temperature changed?

2. Use the graduated cylinder to pour 250 ml of ice water into another beaker. Use the thermometer to determine the exact temperature of the ice water. Prepare a second light stick as you did in step 1, and put it in the ice water. After five minutes, remove the light stick from the beaker and check the temperature of the water again. Has it changed? Describe the appearance of the light stick. How does it compare with the light stick that was in the beaker with room-temperature water?

3. Use the graduated cylinder to pour 250 ml of hot water into the third beaker. Use the thermometer to determine the exact temperature of the hot water. (CAUTION: Be sure that the temperature of the water is not greater than 70° C.) Prepare the third light stick as you did the other two, put it in the hot water, and remove it after five minutes. Check the temperature of the hot water. Has it changed? Describe the appearance of this light stick. How does it compare with the other two?

4. Place the three light sticks side by side on a table. Compare the intensity of light that each produces.

*(continued)*

Name_____ Date _____

# How Do Chemicals Produce Light? *(continued)*

 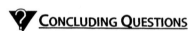 DATA COLLECTION AND ANALYSIS

1. Describe the color and position of the glow **emitted** by the first light stick.

2. In the table below, write your observations of the three light sticks.

| Light Stick | Water Temp. at Start | Water Temp. at Finish | Intensity of Glow After Immersion |
|---|---|---|---|
| #1 (room temp.) | | | |
| #2 (ice water) | | | |
| #3 (hot water) | | | |

3. What is the effect of temperature on the intensity of light that the light sticks produce?

4. Did the reaction that produced light also produce heat? What evidence do you have to support your statement?

## ? CONCLUDING QUESTIONS

Write your answers to the following questions on the back of this sheet.

1. Why was the first light stick placed in water at room temperature?

2. Why was the water temperature checked both before and after immersing the light sticks?

3. What was the reason for using water at different temperatures?

4. Assuming that all of the light sticks contained the same amount of chemicals, which of the three do you hypothesize would fade first? Explain your answer.

5. Design an experiment to test your hypothesis concerning which light stick would fade first.

---

### 📬 FOLLOW-UP ACTIVITIES 📬

1. Take one of the light sticks home and put it in the freezer overnight. Observe the effect of placing the light stick in the freezer. Observe what happens after it is allowed to return to room temperature and left out for one, two, and five hours. Write your observations in a report.

2. Devise an experiment to test how freezing and thawing a light stick affects chemiluminescence.

3. Research bioluminescence.

4. Report on how a firefly produces light.

---

## INSTRUCTIONAL OBJECTIVES

Students will be able to:

- record observations.
- state the law of reflection.
- demonstrate the law of reflection.
- draw conclusions based on observations.
- explain the law of reflection to other students.

 ## NATIONAL SCIENCE STANDARDS ADDRESSED

Students demonstrate understanding of

- how a plane mirror reflects light.

Students demonstrate scientific inquiry and problem-solving skills by

- identifying and controlling variables in an experimental research setting.
- identifying a problem and evaluating the outcomes of its investigation.
- working individually and in teams to collect and share information and ideas.

Students demonstrate effective scientific communication by

- arguing from evidence.
- explaining scientific concepts to other students.

 ## MATERIALS

- Plane mirror with support
- Four pieces of white paper
- Cardboard
- Pins
- Protractor
- Ruler

### HELPFUL HINTS AND DISCUSSION

**Time frame:** One period
**Structure:** Individual students or cooperative learning groups
**Location:** In class or at home

In this activity, students make observations about light reflected by a plane mirror and deduce the law of reflection. Commercial kits to perform this activity are available, or you can put together the material yourself. The mirror must be supported, either glued to a block of wood or held in place with pieces of clay. It might be helpful to demonstrate the law of reflection with a blackboard optics kit before the students do this activity.

### ADAPTATIONS FOR HIGH AND LOW ACHIEVERS

**High Achievers:** Encourage these students to do the follow-up activities.

**Low Achievers:** Provide a glossary and reference material for boldfaced terms in this activity. Organize these students into cooperative learning groups, each of which should include students of higher ability.

### SCORING RUBRIC

Full credit should be given to students who complete the data tables and correctly answer all questions, using full sentences. Extra credit should be given for completing follow-up activities.

 ## INTERNET TIE-INS

http://nyelabs.kcts.org/nyeverse/episode/e27.html
http://www.sciencenow.org
http://odin.phys.bris.ac.uk8080
http:www.yahoo.com/Science/Education/
http:www.mos.org/

 ## QUIZ

1. According to the law of reflection, what is the relationship between the angle of incidence and the angle of reflection?
2. Will a light ray be reflected if it strikes a plane mirror at an angle of 35°? Explain your answer.

Name_____ Date _____

# How Does a Plane Mirror Reflect Light?

## � BEFORE YOU BEGIN ✥

Today you are going to investigate the way light is reflected by a **plane mirror**. A plane mirror is one that is flat, not curved. To do this activity, you need to be familiar with some of the terms used to describe the behavior of light. A light ray that comes toward a surface, such as a mirror, is called the **incident ray**. A light ray that a surface reflects, or sends back, is called the **reflected ray**. A line drawn perpendicular to the mirror is called the **normal**. The angle formed between the incident ray and the normal is called the **angle of incidence**. The angle formed between the normal and the reflected ray is called the **angle of reflection**. The diagram will help you to understand these terms.

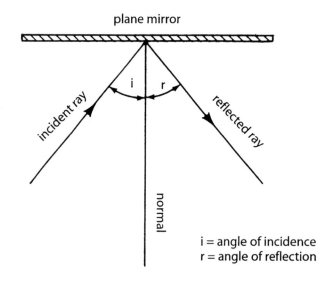

plane mirror

incident ray    i   r    reflected ray

normal

i = angle of incidence
r = angle of reflection

##  MATERIALS

- Plane mirror with support
- Four pieces of white paper
- Cardboard

- Pins
- Protractor
- Ruler

*(continued)*

         *Walch Hands-on Science Series: Light and Color*

## How Does a Plane Mirror Reflect Light? *(continued)*

 ### PROCEDURE

1. Place the first piece of white paper on the cardboard. Then stand the mirror upright on the paper at one end of the cardboard. The **reflective** surface of the mirror should face the length of paper. (See diagram.)

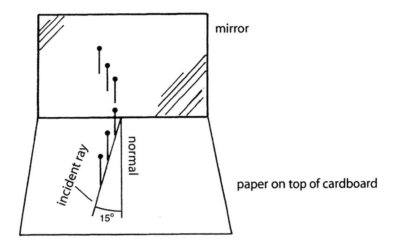

2. Draw a perpendicular line, starting where the mirror meets the paper, down the length of the paper, as illustrated in the diagram. This line is called the **normal**. Label it.

3. Use the protractor to draw an incident ray that makes a 15° angle with the normal. This is the **angle of incidence**.

4. Place the straight pins at an equal distance from one other along the line of the incident ray, approximately 2 cm apart. Make sure that all pins are exactly on the line and that they are standing straight up. (See the diagram.)

5. Now, look into the mirror. You will see a line of pins that seems to extend back into the mirror. Describe the position of this line as it appears in the mirror in relation to its actual position on the paper. Stick three or four more pins into the cardboard so that they seem to continue the line of pins you see in the mirror. It is important that you position the pins about 2 cm apart to form a straight and continuous line from the image in the mirror toward you.

6. Draw a line that connects the pins you have just added. This line represents the **reflected ray**. Measure the angle formed between the reflected ray and the normal.

7. Record your measurement of this **angle of reflection** in the Data Collection and Analysis section.

8. Repeat steps 1–7 using fresh sheets of paper with the angle of incidence drawn at 30°, 45°, and 60°. Record the angle of reflection for each angle of incidence in the data table.

*(continued)*

## How Does a Plane Mirror Reflect Light? *(continued)*

 **DATA COLLECTION AND ANALYSIS**

### Data Table

| Angle of Incidence | Angle of Reflection |
|:---:|:---:|
| 15° | |
| 30° | |
| 45° | |
| 60° | |

Record your answers to the following questions on the back of this sheet.

**CONCLUDING QUESTIONS**

1. Based on the data you have collected, what is the relationship between the angle of incidence and the angle of reflection in the four cases you studied?

2. Look up the law of reflection in a textbook. Do your data support the law? Explain your reasoning.

3. Write a brief explanation of what you have learned about the law of reflection for your classmates.

4. You have been asked to set up a security mirror inside your classroom to observe what happens in the hallway. Where in the classroom would you locate this mirror? Explain your reasoning.

---

### 🔨 FOLLOW-UP ACTIVITIES 🔨

1. Do this activity with various angles of incidence—for example, 25°, 75°.

2. What are some possible sources of error in this activity?

3. Another way to do this activity is to tape a comb with large spaces between the teeth to the front of a light source, like a flashlight. The comb will separate the light into individual rays, so you can trace one ray of light as it is reflected by a mirror. Use this method to confirm your findings about the law of reflection.

4. Research the use of mirrors in periscopes.

5. Research the use of mirrors in kaleidoscopes.

---

# How Does Light Affect Light-Sensitive Chemicals?

 **INSTRUCTIONAL OBJECTIVES**

Students will be able to

- record observations.
- explain how light intensities affect light-sensitive chemicals.
- draw conclusions based on observations.

 **NATIONAL SCIENCE STANDARDS ADDRESSED**

Students demonstrate understanding of

- light-sensitive chemicals.
- interactions between light and matter.

Students demonstrate scientific inquiry and problem-solving skills by

- using physical science concepts to explain observations.
- evaluating the outcome of an investigation.
- working individually or in teams to collect and share information and ideas.
- identifying and controlling experimental variables.

Students demonstrate effective scientific communication by

- arguing from evidence.
- explaining scientific concepts to other students.

Students demonstrate competence with the tools and technologies of science by

- using equipment and materials.

 **MATERIALS**

- Five pieces of light-sensitive paper
- Lamp with 40- or 60-watt incandescent bulb
- Object (key or coin)
- Black paper
- Scissors
- Black-and-white negative
- Glass plate
- Water bath
- Forceps

## HELPFUL HINTS AND DISCUSSION

**Time frame:** One period
**Structure:** Individual students or cooperative learning groups
**Location:** In class

You can purchase light-sensitive paper from a supply house or make it according to the instructions below. *Do not use* photographic paper, which is too sensitive for this exercise. The photosensitive solution is made by combining two solutions (A and B) in a darkened room (no direct light). These chemicals are available from any science supply company.

Solution A:
Dissolve 30 g of potassium hexacyanoferrate(III) $K_3Fe(CN)_6$ in 100 ml of water.

Solution B:
Dissolve 40 g of ammonium citrate in 100 ml of water.

In a darkened room, use a sponge to coat ordinary bond paper with the photosensitive solution and allow it to dry. Cut the sheets into four equal pieces. Keep the prepared paper in a box to prevent exposure to light.

*(continued)*

| | |
|---|---|
| **ADAPTATIONS FOR HIGH AND LOW ACHIEVERS**<br><br>**High Achievers:** Encourage these students to do the follow-up activities, particularly activities 1 and 4.<br>**Low Achievers:** Motivate students for this activity with a demonstration, such as exposure of AgCl to light, or with a discussion of photosensitive chemicals. | **SCORING RUBRIC**<br><br>Full credit should be given to students who record observations and answer all questions correctly, using full sentences. Extra credit should be given for completing follow-up activities. |

 **INTERNET TIE-INS**

hhtp://www.yahoo.com/Science/Education
hhtp://abell.austinc.edu/dag/resource/history/history.html
hhtp://www.ahfmr.ab.ca/march/fungus.html
http://www.wildstar.net/~doswell/Outdoor_Images/Photo_Basics.html
hhtp://www.kodak.com

 **QUIZ**

1. Why are some chemicals stored in dark bottles?
2. Describe the behavior of light-sensitive chemicals when they are exposed to light.

# How Does Light Affect Light-Sensitive Chemicals?

### ✄ BEFORE YOU BEGIN ✄

Many chemicals are sensitive to light and will change colors when exposed to light. For example, paper and fabrics may fade with exposure to sunlight; people's skin color darkens in the sun; and light-sensitive lenses darken when exposed to light. Photography depends on light-sensitive film. In fact, the word *photograph* means "to make a picture with light." In this activity, you will investigate the effect of light on light-sensitive chemicals.

## MATERIALS

- Five pieces of light-sensitive paper
- Lamp with 40- or 60-watt incandescent bulb
- Object (key or coin)
- Black paper
- Scissors

- Black-and-white negative
- Glass plate
- Water bath
- Forceps

## PROCEDURE

Record your observations and answers to questions in the Data Collection and Analysis section. Carry out all of the procedures in a darkened room. Keep the light-sensitive paper covered until you are ready to use it.

1. Place the lamp on your desk, but don't turn it on. Remove a piece of light-sensitive paper from its package and place it on the desk. Put an object (key or coin) on top of the paper. Turn on the light and leave it on for two minutes. DO NOT MOVE either the object or the paper during this period. Turn the light off and remove the object from the light-sensitive paper. Holding the paper with forceps, dip it in the water bath several times, remove it, and let it dry. Examine the paper carefully and record your observations.

2. Repeat step 1, but leave the lamp on for four minutes. Record your observations.

3. Repeat step 1, but increase the exposure time to six minutes. Record your observations.

4. Cut a piece of black paper in a shape of your choosing (for example, an animal, a person, a heart). Place it on an unexposed piece of light-sensitive paper and expose it to light for three to five minutes. Dip the exposed paper in the water bath several times, using the forceps to hold it. On the back of your paper, make a drawing that shows how the image of the cutout looks on the light-sensitive paper. Indicate the color of both image and background paper.

5. Place a black-and-white negative on a piece of light-sensitive paper and cover it with a glass plate. Turn on the light for five minutes. Dip the light-sensitive paper in the water bath. Describe what you see on the light-sensitive paper.

*(continued)*

## How Does Light Affect Light-Sensitive Chemicals? *(continued)*

 DATA COLLECTION AND ANALYSIS

### Data Table

| Sample & Object | Exposure Time | Description (describe what you see, and indicate the color of the image and the background) |
|---|---|---|
| 1 | 2 min. | |
| 2 | 4 min. | |
| 3 | 6 min. | |
| 4 (black paper cutout) | 3–5 min. | |
| 5 (negative) | 5 min. | |

6. How does the image created with the black-and-white negative differ from the image formed using the key or coin?

_____

_____

_____

_____

_____

_____

_____

*(continued)*

## How Does Light Affect Light-Sensitive Chemicals? *(continued)*

### ❓ CONCLUDING QUESTIONS

1. How did increasing the exposure time affect the image produced on the color-sensitive paper?

   _____

   _____

   _____

2. How can you account for the differences in the images formed by the negative and by the object?

   _____

   _____

   _____

3. Hypothesize how changing the intensity of light might affect the light-sensitive paper.

   _____

   _____

   _____

4. What was the purpose of dipping the paper in a water bath after exposing it to light?

   _____

   _____

   _____

5. Some chemicals, including some medicines, are kept in brown bottles or are labeled "store in dark." What reasons can you give for this?

   _____

   _____

   _____

---

### 🔦 FOLLOW-UP ACTIVITIES 🔦

1. Design an experiment to test the effect of different light intensities on photosensitive paper.

2. Research the history of daguerreotypes.

3. Using the library and other resources, write a report about the history of photography.

4. Research the use of photosensitive chemicals in treating cancer. Present this information to your classmates.

# How Is White Light Separated into Colors?

 **INSTRUCTIONAL OBJECTIVES**

Students will be able to

- record observations.
- identify white light as being composed of light of different colors.
- identify and explain the effect of colored filters on spectra.
- explain the wave nature of light.
- define the terms *prism, diffraction, amplitude, wavelength, continuous spectrum.*
- draw conclusions based on observations.

**NATIONAL SCIENCE STANDARDS ADDRESSED**

Students demonstrate understanding of

- the visible spectrum.
- interactions between light and matter.

Students demonstrate scientific inquiry and problem-solving skills by

- using physical science concepts to explain observations.
- working in teams to collect and share information and ideas.

Students demonstrate effective scientific communication by

- arguing from evidence.
- explaining scientific concepts to other students.

Students demonstrate competence with the tools and technologies of science by

- using a spectroscope.

 **MATERIALS**

- Student spectroscope
- Light filters (red, blue, green, orange)
- Lamp with 40- or 60-watt incandescent bulb
- Prism
- Flashlight with concentrated beam
- White paper screen

## HELPFUL HINTS AND DISCUSSION

**Time frame:** One period
**Structure:** Cooperative learning groups of two or more students
**Location:** In class

Student spectroscopes (a tube with a diffraction grating at one end and a slit cut in the cardboard at the other) are available from most scientific supply companies at fairly low cost. **Be sure to caution students not to point spectroscopes directly at the sun.** To introduce this activity you might demonstrate the spectrum, using either a prism or a diffraction grating. Using an overhead projector and a diffraction grating is particularly effective. To carry out this demonstration, cover the stage of the projector with a piece of opaque paper that has a slit cut into it, and cover the projector lens with a large diffraction grating.

As you work with color filters, you will find that they transmit light of various wavelengths, so the spectrum they create will consist of several colors: The red filter may transmit red and yellow light; the blue filter may transmit blue and green.

## ADAPTATIONS FOR HIGH AND LOW ACHIEVERS

**High Achievers:** These students should be held to a more sophisticated understanding of the wave nature of light and of spectra. Encourage these students to do the follow-up activities, particularly activities 2 and 3.

**Low Achievers:** Provide a glossary and reference material for boldfaced terms in this activity. Introduce the concept of light waves, the properties of waves, and the relation between color and wavelength.

## SCORING RUBRIC

Full credit should be given to students who record observations and answer all questions correctly, using full sentences. Extra credit should be given for completing follow-up activities.

*(continued)*

 **INTERNET TIE-INS**    hhtp://www.yahoo.com/science/education
http:/asd-www.larc.nasa.gov/edu_act/simple_spec.html
http://FusionEd.gat.com
http://www.astrowashington.edu/astro101/LABS
http://129.82.166.181/CD_Spectroscope/html
http://www.geom.umn.edu

 **QUIZ**
1. How is a diffraction grating similar to a prism?
2. What happens to white light when it passes through a diffraction grating?
3. How do we recognize differences in wavelengths of light?
4. What does a red filter do to white light?

# How Is White Light Separated into Colors?

### 🎇 BEFORE YOU BEGIN 🎇

One way of picturing light is as a wave. You are already familiar with some types of waves in nature—for example, water waves. Like water waves, light waves can vary in height, or **amplitude**, and in length, or **wavelength**. The diagram below shows a wave's amplitude and wavelength.

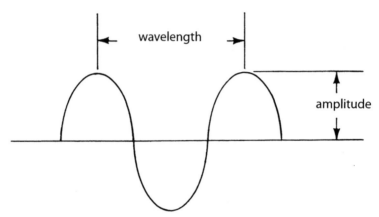

The human eye sees different wavelengths of light as different colors. White light, such as that from a lightbulb or the sun, is actually made up of many different wavelengths of light. Today you are going to separate white light into its components, using a **spectroscope** and a **prism**. A spectroscope contains a diffraction grating that bends light of different wavelengths different amounts. A prism does the same thing. Using either of these tools, you can separate white light into its component wavelengths (colors). The range of colors that results is called a **visible spectrum**. When you see a rainbow, you are seeing a visible spectrum produced by nature.

## MATERIALS

- Student spectroscope
- Light filters (red, blue, green, orange)
- Lamp with 40- or 60-watt incandescent bulb
- Prism
- Flashlight with concentrated beam
- White paper screen

## PROCEDURE

Record your observations and answers to questions in the Data Collection and Analysis section.

1. Using one eye, look through the diffraction grating of the spectroscope tube with the slit at the other end pointed toward a window. Aim the spectroscope toward the sky through the window. **CAUTION: Do not aim it directly at the sun because you can burn your eye.** You will see light coming through the slit. If the slit is not vertical, rotate the end of the tube until it is.

*(continued)*

Name_____ Date _____

## How Is White Light Separated into Colors? *(continued)*

Look to the left and right of the slit to see the spectrum. In the Data Collection section, describe the colors of the spectrum and the order of the colors. Make a drawing of the spectrum, indicating the relative size of each band of color.

2. Repeat step 1, using an incandescent bulb as the light source. Once again, record and draw your observations in the Data Collection section.

3. Looking through the spectroscope, aim it toward an incandescent lightbulb. Place a red filter in front of the spectroscope so that only red light is seen. In the Data Collection section, describe the colors of the spectrum in the order that you see them. Make a drawing of the spectrum, indicating the relative size of each band of color.

4. Repeat step 3 with a blue filter, a green filter, and an orange filter.

5. Place a prism in front of the screen and shine light from the flashlight through it. Project the spectrum on the screen. In the Data Collection section, describe the colors of the spectrum and the order of the colors. Make a drawing of the spectrum, indicating the relative size of each band of color.

 **DATA COLLECTION AND ANALYSIS**

**Data Table**

| Light Source | Order of Colors (R = red, O = orange Y = yellow, G = green B = blue, I = indigo V = violet) | Drawing of Spectrum |
|---|---|---|
| Sunlight | | |
| Incandescent bulb | | |

*(continued)*

## How Is White Light Separated into Colors? *(continued)*

### Data Table (continued)

| Light Source | Order of Colors (R = red, O = orange Y = yellow, G = green B = blue, I = indigo V = violet) | Drawing of Spectrum |
|---|---|---|
| Incandescent bulb + red filter | | |
| Incandescent bulb + blue filter | | |
| Incandescent bulb + green filter | | |
| Incandescent bulb + orange filter | | |

6. Describe and draw the spectrum produced with a prism. Does it differ from the spectrum produced with a spectroscope?

_____

_____

_____

*(continued)*

## How Is White Light Separated into Colors? *(continued)*

### ❓ CONCLUDING QUESTIONS

1. For your classmates, write a brief explanation of what you have learned about the visible spectrum.

   _____

   _____

   _____

2. How do filters affect the light that passes through them? Support your answer with evidence from this activity.

   _____

   _____

   _____

3. When you passed light through a red filter, did it transmit only red light? Support your answer with evidence from your investigation.

   _____

   _____

   _____

4. What is the difference between the spectra produced by diffraction gratings and prisms?

   _____

   _____

5. With the help of drawings, explain how the light waves of red and blue light differ.

   _____

   _____

   _____

---

### 🔦 FOLLOW-UP ACTIVITIES 🔦

1. Using the spectroscope, investigate the spectra produced by fluorescent bulbs or sodium lamps.
2. Investigate and report on the use of spectroscopes in astronomy.
3. Investigate the electromagnetic spectrum and the place of visible light in it.
4. Research electromagnetic waves and report your findings to the class.
5. Research and write a report about how rainbows form.

# What Determines the Color of an Object?

## ✔ INSTRUCTIONAL OBJECTIVES

Students will be able to

- record observations.
- explain that an object's color depends on the color of the illuminating light.
- predict what color an object will reflect when it is illuminated by a particular color of light.
- draw conclusions based on observations.

## 🌐 NATIONAL SCIENCE STANDARDS ADDRESSED

Students demonstrate understanding of

- dependence of an object's color on the color of the illuminating light.
- interactions between light and matter.

Students demonstrate scientific inquiry and problem-solving skills by

- using physical science concepts to explain observations.
- identifying a problem and evaluating the outcomes of its investigation.

Students demonstrate effective scientific communication by

- arguing from evidence.
- explaining scientific concepts to other students.
- working individually and in teams to collect and share information and ideas.

Students demonstrate competence with the tools and technologies of science by

- constructing an experimental apparatus.

##  MATERIALS

- Cardboard box
- Scissors
- Masking tape
- Flashlight
- Red, blue, green, and orange filters
- Red, blue, green, orange, and white construction paper
- Glue stick
- Ruler

## HELPFUL HINTS AND DISCUSSION

**Time frame:**  Two periods
**Structure:**  Individual students or cooperative learning groups
**Location:**  In class or at home

Any cardboard box can be used (e.g., shoe box, gift box) provided that it has a separate lid. Any holes in the box should be covered with masking tape to prevent light leaks.

## ADAPTATIONS FOR HIGH AND LOW ACHIEVERS

**High Achievers:** Encourage these students to do the follow-up activities, particularly activities 2 and 3.

**Low Achievers:** These students should be supervised when they construct the viewing box. Review the data table with these students and explain the type of data expected. Organize these students into cooperative learning groups, each of which should include students of higher ability.

## SCORING RUBRIC

Full credit should be given to students who record observations and correctly answer all questions, using full sentences. Extra credit should be given for completing follow-up activities.

*(continued)*

64

 **INTERNET TIE-INS**    http://www.yahoo.com/Science/Education/
http://www.sciencenow.org
http://www.exploratorium.edu/light
http://odin.phy.bris.ac.uk.8080/dr_nutrino/index.html

 **QUIZ**    What color will a red object reflect when illuminated with blue light? Explain.

Name_____   Date _____

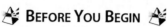

---

 **BEFORE YOU BEGIN**

Have you ever bought a piece of clothing and found that it was a different color at home than it appeared to be when you saw it in the store? We can see an object only if it is **luminous** or **illuminated**. An illuminated object is visible because it reflects some of the **illuminating light**. The reason your clothing seemed to be a different color in the store was because the light that illuminated it was a different color than the light that illuminated it at home. In this activity, you will investigate how the color of illuminating light affects an object's appearance. To do this, you will construct a viewing box that will allow you to control the color of light in it.

---

##  MATERIALS

- Cardboard box
- Scissors
- Masking tape
- Flashlight

- Red, blue, green, and orange filters
- Red, blue, green, orange, and white construction paper
- Glue stick
- Ruler

## PROCEDURE

Record your observations and answers to questions in the Data Collection and Analysis section. Carry out steps 4–8 in a darkened room.

1. Cut a square hole, approximately 3 cm × 5 cm, in one end of the top of your cardboard box, as shown in the diagram. This hole, called the **illumination hole**, allows illuminating light to enter the box.

2. Cut a hole approximately 3 cm × 5 cm in the side of the box, opposite the end where you cut the illumination hole. This hole, the **observation hole**, allows you to observe an object in the box.

3. Cut 6-cm × 8-cm pieces of white, red, blue, and orange paper.

4. Fold the white piece of paper in half lengthwise, as shown. Open the lid and place the folded paper so it stands in the box directly beneath the illumination hole and faces the observation hole, as shown in the diagram. Place the lid back on the box. Put the flashlight over the illumination hole and turn it on. Look through the observation hole. Record the color of the white paper.

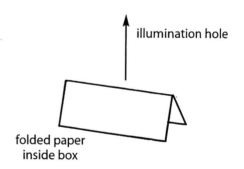

illumination hole

observation hole

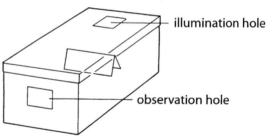

illumination hole

folded paper
inside box

*(continued)*

## What Determines the Color of an Object? *(continued)*

5. Place a red filter over the illumination hole and shine the flashlight through it. Look through the observation hole and record the appearance of the white paper under red light.

6. Repeat step 5 using a blue and then an orange filter.

7. Fold the 6 × 8 piece of red paper in half lengthwise. Remove the lid and replace the white paper with red paper so the red paper is beneath the illumination hole. Replace the lid on the box. Put the flashlight over the illumination hole and turn it on. Look through the observation hole. Record the color of the red paper.

8. Place a red filter over the illumination hole and shine the flashlight through it. Look through the observation hole and record the color of the red paper under red light.

9. Repeat step 8 using a blue and then an orange filter.

10. Fold the 6 × 8 piece of blue paper in half lengthwise. Remove the lid and replace the red paper beneath the illumination hole with the blue paper. Put the lid back on the box. Put the flashlight over the illumination hole and turn it on. Look through the observation hole and record the color of the blue paper under white light.

11. Place a red filter over the illumination hole and shine the flashlight through it. Look through the observation hole and record the color of the blue paper under red light.

12. Repeat step 11 using a blue and then an orange filter.

13. Fold the 6 × 8 piece of green paper in half. Remove the lid and replace the blue paper beneath the illumination hole with the green paper. Replace the lid. Put the flashlight over the illumination hole and turn it on. Look through the observation hole and record the appearance of the blue paper under white light.

14. Place a red filter over the illumination hole and shine the flashlight through it. Look through the observation hole and record the color of the green paper under red light.

15. Repeat step 14 using a blue and then an orange filter.

16. Cut small pieces of red paper and paste them on a piece of blue paper. Fold this piece of paper in half and place it in the box, after removing the green paper. Replace the lid. Put the flashlight over the illumination hole and turn it on. Look through the observation hole. Record the appearance of the red and blue paper under white light.

17. Place a red filter over the illumination hole and shine the flashlight through it. Look through the observation hole and record the color of the red and blue paper under red light.

18. Repeat step 17 using a blue and then an orange filter.

*(continued)*

Name_____    Date _____

19. With colored paper and the glue stick, construct another color pattern, similar to that in step 16, using two or three colors. Predict the effects of white, red, and blue light on the pattern you made.

20. Test your hypothesis using the observation box and colored filters. Record your expected results of viewing the color pattern under different lights and what you actually observe.

 DATA COLLECTION AND ANALYSIS

### Data Table

| Object Color (paper in box) | Light Color Coming Through Illumination Hole | Apparent Color Seen Through Observation Hole |
|---|---|---|
| white | white | |
| white | red | |
| white | blue | |
| white | orange | |
| red | white | |
| red | red | |
| red | blue | |
| red | orange | |
| blue | white | |
| blue | red | |
| blue | blue | |
| blue | orange | |
| green | white | |
| green | red | |
| green | blue | |
| green | orange | |
| red and blue | white | |
| red and blue | red | |
| red and blue | blue | |
| red and blue | orange | |

*(continued)*

## What Determines the Color of an Object? *(continued)*

1. On the back of this sheet, draw and label the color pattern created in step 19.

2. Indicate in the table below the color pattern you expected to see under white, red, and blue light.

3. How did the pattern you predicted compare with the actual color pattern you observed under white, red, and blue light?

| Filter Color | Predicted Color Pattern | Observed Color Pattern |
|:---:|:---:|:---:|
| white | | |
| red | | |
| blue | | |

### 🎯 CONCLUDING QUESTIONS

Record your answers to the following questions on the back of this sheet.

1. Based on your observations, write a general statement that describes the relationship between illuminating light and the apparent color of an object.

2. What colors of illuminating light does an object reflect? Support your statement with examples from this activity.

3. What colors of illuminating light does an object absorb? Support your statement with examples from this activity.

4. Fluorescent lights produce wavelengths of light different from those of incandescent light-bulbs. Why do fabrics look different under these two kinds of light?

---

### 🎇 FOLLOW-UP ACTIVITIES 🎇

1. Put together different combinations of colored paper and test the effect of different filters on these color combinations.

2. Research the use of color gels on spotlights in theater design.

3. Investigate how interior designers use different kinds of lights.

4. Explain why rooms photographed in daylight may look different when photographed under artificial light. How can this be corrected?

5. Research and report to the class on how light is used in supermarket displays.

---

# What Happens When Different Colors of Light Are Mixed by Addition or Subtraction?

 **INSTRUCTIONAL OBJECTIVES**

Students will be able to

- record observations.
- explain how colors change when mixed by subtraction.
- describe the effect of mixing of colors by addition.
- draw conclusions based on observations.

 **NATIONAL SCIENCE STANDARDS ADDRESSED**

Students demonstrate understanding of:

- mixing colors.
- interactions between light and matter.

Students demonstrate scientific inquiry and problem-solving skills by

- using physical science concepts to explain observations.
- evaluating the outcomes of an investigation.

Students demonstrate effective scientific communication by

- arguing from evidence.
- explaining scientific concepts to other students.
- working individually and in teams to collect and share information and ideas.

Students demonstrate competence with the tools and technologies of science by

- using color filters.

 **MATERIALS**

- Flashlight
- Magenta, cyan, yellow, red, blue, and green filters
- Sheets of paper
- Colored markers (red, blue, and yellow)
- Metric ruler

## HELPFUL HINTS AND DISCUSSION

**Time frame:** One period
**Structure:** Individual students or cooperative learning groups
**Location:** In class

As an introduction to this activity, demonstrate additive mixing, showing how adding red, blue, and green light produces white light. Then, demonstrate mixing red and blue light to produce magenta and mixing blue and green light to produce cyan. Finally, mix red and green light to produce yellow. You can use either an additive light mixing apparatus or three projectors, each with a different color filter, for the demonstration. Use colored markers that are transparent. Any brand will do as long as the markers aren't completely opaque.

## ADAPTATIONS FOR HIGH AND LOW ACHIEVERS

**High Achievers:** Encourage these students to do the follow-up activities, particularly activities 1 and 2.

**Low Achievers:** Provide a glossary and reference material for boldfaced terms in this activity. Review the data table with these students. You will need to differentiate between additive and subtractive color mixing and help students explain their observations.

## SCORING RUBRIC

Full credit should be given to students who record observations and correctly answer all questions, using full sentences. Extra credit should be given for completing follow-up activities.

*(continued)*

 **INTERNET TIE-INS**
hhtp://www.yahoo.com/Science/Education/
hhtp://wwwmos.org
http://oldsci.eiu.edu/physics/DDavis/1050/Ch17Color/Add.html
http://www.yorku.ca
http://www.thetech.org/hyper/color/
http://www.tomruley.com/Photoshop_pages/Color.html

 **QUIZ**   1. Explain why mixing magenta pigment and cyan pigment will produce a green color.
2. Explain the difference between additive and subtractive mixing of color.

## What Happens When Different Colors of Light Are Mixed by Addition or Subtraction?

STUDENT ACTIVITY PAGE

### ✄ BEFORE YOU BEGIN ✄

Mixing red light and blue light produces a color called magenta. Mixing blue light and green light produces light of a blue-green color called cyan. Mixing red light and green light produces yellow light. Mixing red, blue, and green light produces white light. However, mixing paints in these same colors will not produce the same colors that mixing the colored lights did. When you combine red, blue, and green paints, the mixture absorbs most of the wavelengths of light, so you see only a gray or muddy brown color.

The reason for this difference is that when lights are mixed together, you are mixing them by addition. In **additive mixing**, the wavelengths of two lights are combined to produce a color that contains both wavelengths. When you combine red, blue, and green light, your mind *adds* all of them up and you see white light.

When you combine pigments or light filters, you are mixing colors by **subtraction**. In the previous activity, you learned that an object reflects light of the same color as itself and absorbs all other wavelengths of light. A red object reflects red light and absorbs blue and green, and a blue object reflects blue light and absorbs red and green. Filters transmit light of the wavelength associated with their color and absorb other wavelengths of light. When you mix light beams, you are adding different wavelengths of light; the result is a combination of colors. When you mix pigments or overlap filters, you are subtracting light of particular wavelengths from the original combination. In this activity, you will mix colors by subtraction and observe the effects.

 MATERIALS

- Flashlight
- Magenta, cyan, yellow, red, blue, and green filters
- Sheets of white paper

- Colored markers (red, blue, and yellow)
- Metric ruler

 PROCEDURE

Record your observations in the table found in the Data Collection and Analysis section.

1. Hold the magenta filter to the light and notice the color of light passing through it. Hold the cyan filter to the light and notice the color of light passing through it. Now overlap the magenta filter with the cyan filter and observe the color of light that you see through the two filters together. In Table I, record the colors of each of the two filters, the color you see looking through each filter, and finally, the color seen when you overlap (mix) both filters. To help you get started, most of the information for the first pair of filters has already been entered in the table.

2. Repeat step 1 with the magenta filter and the yellow filter.

3. Repeat step 1 with the yellow filter and the cyan filter.

4. Combine all three filters and describe the color you see.

*(continued)*

## What Happens When Different Colors of Light Are Mixed by Addition or Subtraction? *(continued)*

5. On a sheet of white paper, make a mark approximately 1 cm × 3 cm with a red marker. Go over the red mark with a blue marker. Record the color you see after the two markers have been combined in Table II.

6. Repeat step 5 with red and yellow markers.

7. Repeat step 5 with red and blue markers.

 **DATA COLLECTION AND ANALYSIS**

### Table I

| Color of Filter 1 | Component Colors of Filter 1 | Color of Filter 2 | Component Colors of Filter 2 | Observed Color After Overlapping (Mixing) Filters 1 and 2 |
|---|---|---|---|---|
| Magenta | red + blue | cyan | blue + green | |
| | | | | |
| | | | | |

1. The color seen when magenta, yellow, and cyan filters were combined is

_____

2. For each combination of filters listed in Table I, circle any color that is a component of both filter 1 and filter 2. (For example, in the first row of the table, you would circle "blue.")

### Table II

| Color of Marker 1 | Color of Marker 2 | Color Observed After Mixing |
|---|---|---|
| | | |
| | | |
| | | |

3. Predict the result of mixing different combinations of markers and test your predictions.

4. What did you learn by circling the colors in Table I?

*(continued)*

## What Happens When Different Colors of Light Are Mixed by Addition or Subtraction? *(continued)*

### ❓ CONCLUDING QUESTIONS

1. How can you account for the result of mixing magenta and cyan?

   _____

   _____

2. How can you account for the result of mixing magenta and yellow?

   _____

   _____

3. How can you account for the result of mixing yellow and cyan?

   _____

   _____

4. Compare the results of mixing pigments with the results of mixing filters.

   _____

   _____

5. Write a general statement to describe mixing colors by subtraction.

   _____

   _____

   _____

---

### 📬 FOLLOW-UP ACTIVITIES 📬

1. Research how the human eye perceives color.

2. Using food coloring, investigate what happens when a color is mixed with itself—for example, when two samples of yellow food coloring are mixed.

3. Investigate the result of subtractive mixing using food coloring and gelatin desserts. For example, mix yellow gelatin with blue gelatin.

4. Research mixing colors in television screens.

# Why Do the Colors of a Soap Bubble Change?

## ✔️ INSTRUCTIONAL OBJECTIVES

Students will be able to

- record observations.
- explain interference.
- demonstrate the wave nature of light.
- draw conclusions based on observations.

## 🌐 NATIONAL SCIENCE STANDARDS ADDRESSED

Students demonstrate understanding of

- interference.
- the wave nature of light.
- interactions between light and matter.

Students demonstrate scientific inquiry and problem-solving skills by

- using physical science concepts to explain observations.
- identifying a problem and evaluating the outcomes of its investigation.

Students demonstrate effective scientific communication by

- arguing from evidence.
- representing data and results in multiple ways.
- explaining scientific concepts to other students.
- working in teams to collect and share information and ideas.

Students demonstrate competence with the tools and technologies of science by

- using a light filter and a watch and constructing an apparatus.

##  MATERIALS

- Two-ply poster board
- Scissors
- Ruler
- Tape
- Soap solution
- Plastic straw
- Shallow pan
- Red filter (red cellophane)
- Flashlight
- Stopwatch or watch with second hand

## HELPFUL HINTS AND DISCUSSION

**Time frame:** Two periods
**Structure:** Cooperative learning groups
**Location:** In class or at home

Make a soap solution by combining dishwashing liquid, glycerin, and water. For 500 ml of solution, combine 30 ml of dishwashing liquid with 8 drops of glycerin, and add enough water to bring the volume up to 500 ml. Stir to ensure equal mixing. The shallow pans are used to contain the soap solution. They should be made of dark material or have their bottoms covered with smooth, black nonabsorbent paper. A collar is used to prevent air currents from affecting the experiment and to focus light toward the bubble. Make the collar from a piece of two-ply poster board that is nonabsorbent and holds up to soaking. Lighter paper, such as printer paper, can be used, but it tends to absorb the soap solution and get soggy. If you use a lighter paper, try protecting the edge that stands in the solution with plastic packaging tape.

*(continued)*

## ADAPTATIONS FOR HIGH AND LOW ACHIEVERS

**High Achievers:** These students should demonstrate a more sophisticated understanding of the wave nature of light and interference. Encourage these students to perform the follow-up activities, particularly activities 3, 4, and 5.

**Low Achievers:** Provide a glossary and reference material for bold-faced terms in this activity. These students should perform this activity under adult supervision (teacher or parent). You will need to explain interference, and you may have to lead these students through a discussion of interference to explain their observations. However, the main point of the activity for this group is observations and using observations to predict when the bubble will pop, not explaining interference.

## SCORING RUBRIC

Full credit should be given to students who record observations and answer all questions correctly, using full sentences. Extra credit should be given for completing follow-up activities.

 **INTERNET TIE-INS**

http://nyelabs.kcts.org/nyeverse/episode/e27.html
http://www.sciencenow.org
http://scifun.chem.wisc.edu/HOMEEXPTS/SOAPBUBL.html
http//www.journey.sunsyb.edu/Project Java/wavelnt/home.html
http://www.eecs.umich.edu/

 **QUIZ**

1. How will light waves that are in phase interfere with each other?
2. Why does an oil slick on water produce an interference pattern?

Name_____ Date _____

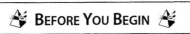
✦ BEFORE YOU BEGIN ✦

In this activity you will explore how a soap bubble reflects light. To understand your observations, it is helpful to think about the structure of a bubble and to learn the theories that explain the nature of light. The wall of a soap bubble has an inner surface and an outer surface. When light is reflected from the bubble, some of the light is reflected by the outer surface; some of the light passes through the bubble and is reflected by the inner surface. The light going toward the bubble is referred to as the incident light.

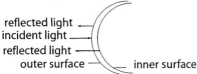
reflected light
incident light
reflected light
outer surface — inner surface

Because there is space between the two surfaces, there is a time lag between the light wave being reflected off the inner surface and the light wave being reflected off the outer surface. Also, after you blow a bubble, it does not stay the same shape. Gravity pulls it downward, making the wall thinner and thinner until the bubble pops. Because of the changing space between the inner and outer surfaces of the bubble wall, we see different patterns of reflected light.

When the light waves reflected by each of the two surfaces combine so that their **crests** are together, they are described as being **in phase**. When this happens, the two waves reinforce each other, producing a brighter band of light. This is called **constructive interference**. In the diagram below, we see two waves combing together to reinforce each other, resulting in a higher **amplitude**.

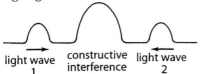
light wave 1    constructive interference    light wave 2

When two light waves combine so that the crest of one and the **trough** of the other are together, they are described as being **out of phase**. When this happens, the two waves cancel each other, producing a dimmer band of light. This is called **destructive interference**. In the diagram below, we see two waves combing together to cancel each other, resulting in a lower amplitude.

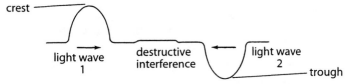
crest
light wave 1    destructive interference    light wave 2    trough

Interference is different for different wavelengths of light and different thicknesses of bubble. Thickness varies with time and with different areas of the bubble wall. Also, the wavelength of reflected light varies, depending on whether it is reflected by the outer surface of the bubble wall or continues on to be reflected off the inner surface. Therefore, different parts of the bubble have different colors. When the bubble wall becomes very thin, there is little difference between the reflected waves, and the bubble appears to have black holes in it. This is due to destructive interference at all wavelengths.

*(continued)* 🔥

## Why Do the Colors of a Soap Bubble Change? *(continued)*

 **MATERIALS**

- Two-ply poster board
- Scissors
- Ruler
- Tape
- Soap solution
- Plastic straw
- Shallow pan (or cafeteria tray)
- Red filter (red cellophane)
- Flashlight
- Stopwatch or watch with second hand

**PROCEDURE**

Record your observations in the Data Collection and Analysis section.

1. Cut a strip of poster board that is approximately 600 cm × 180 cm. Bring the two ends together to form a cylinder, or collar. The ends should overlap. Using tape, fasten the two ends down, taping the seam both inside and outside the collar.

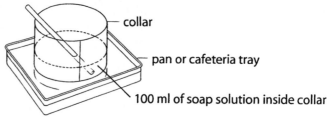

collar

pan or cafeteria tray

100 ml of soap solution inside collar

2. Pour approximately 100 ml of soap solution into the pan and spread it around evenly.

3. Place the collar in the pan, enclosing part of the soap solution.

4. Using the straw, blow a bubble. Then gently remove the straw from the bubble.

5. Have a member of your group observe the colors, color changes, changing color patterns, and changes in brightness. Have another member of your group use a watch to determine the time it takes from when the bubble is formed to its peak brightness, then to the formation of black spots, and finally to the bubble popping. Making these observations will require members of the group to coordinate their responsibilities, so practice with one or two bubbles before you attempt to record experimental data.

6. Repeat your observations with four additional bubbles.

7. Darken the room. Point the beam of the flashlight at the lower part of the inner side of the collar and observe the pattern of colors when bubbles are blown.

*(continued)*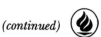

## Why Do the Colors of a Soap Bubble Change? *(continued)*

8. Blow a new bubble. Place the red filter over the flashlight, point the beam of red light toward the same spot on the inner side of the collar, and observe the pattern of colors that you see. It is important to point this beam of light at the side of the collar and not directly at the bubble. You must also do this experiment in a darkened room. How does this pattern differ from what you observed without the filter?

_____

_____

### DATA COLLECTION AND ANALYSIS

1. For each of the five bubbles, record the pattern of colors that you observed.

| Bubble | Colors | Color Changes | Time to Brightest Color | Time to First Black Spots | Time to Pop |
|--------|--------|---------------|-------------------------|---------------------------|-------------|
| Practice A | | | | | |
| Practice B | | | | | |
| 1 | | | | | |
| 2 | | | | | |
| 3 | | | | | |
| 4 | | | | | |
| 5 | | | | | |

Write your answers to questions 2–5 on the back of this sheet.

2. Describe the appearance of the bubble through the red filter.

3. How can you predict when a bubble will burst? Explain your theory in detail.

4. Test your theory of how to predict when a bubble will burst. Explain your results.

5. On the back of this sheet, draw and label a diagram of the pattern of colors that you observed on a bubble's surface.

*(continued)*

## Why Do the Colors of a Soap Bubble Change? *(continued)*

### ❓ CONCLUDING QUESTIONS

1. On the back of this sheet, write a brief newspaper article that explains the pattern of colors on a bubble.

2. Look up *interference* in a textbook. Use this information to explain your observations of the soap bubble.

   _____

   _____

   _____

   _____

3. How did the changing pattern of colors on the soap bubble help predict when the bubble would burst?

   _____

   _____

   _____

   _____

   _____

4. How can you account for the pattern you observed with red light?

   _____

   _____

   _____

   _____

   _____

---

### 🎇 FOLLOW-UP ACTIVITIES 🎇

1. Pour some oil on water and observe the color pattern that forms. Use what you have learned about interference to explain this phenomenon.

2. Research the use of antireflection filters on camera lenses.

3. Why do you think that interference is used as evidence for the wave nature of light theory?

4. Research iridescent colors on the wings of birds and butterflies.

5. Investigate the use of interferometers.

# How Can We Separate Pigments?

## ✔️ INSTRUCTIONAL OBJECTIVES

Students will be able to

- record observations.
- explain how to separate pigments using paper chromatography.
- draw conclusions based on observations.

## 🌐 NATIONAL SCIENCE STANDARDS ADDRESSED

Students demonstrate understanding of

- paper chromatography.
- interactions between light and matter.
- properties of matter.

Students demonstrate scientific inquiry and problem-solving skills by

- using physical science concepts to explain observations.
- identifying a problem and evaluating the outcomes of its investigation.
- working in teams to collect and share information and ideas.

Students demonstrate effective scientific communication by

- arguing from evidence.
- explaining scientific concepts to other students.

Students demonstrate competence with the tools and technologies of science by

- using paper chromatography to separate pigments.
- comparing chromatograms to identify an unknown.

##  MATERIALS

- Two pieces of filter paper
- Eight black water-soluble felt-tip markers of different brands
- Eight pencils
- Scissors
- Eight beakers or other water containers
- Water
- Masking tape
- Metric ruler

## HELPFUL HINTS AND DISCUSSION

**Time frame:** One to two periods
**Structure:** Cooperative learning groups
**Location:** In class or at home

Waftmans #2 or #3 filter paper works well for this activity. If filter paper is unavailable, use coffee filters or paper towels (a commercial grade that is not too absorbent). Select seven brands of black, water-soluble felt-tip markers that yield different patterns when subjected to paper chromatography. (You will have to experiment with a variety of black markers and brands to find seven that produce different patterns.) Label the pens 1 through 7. An additional pen that duplicates one of the seven should be labeled "unknown." Different student groups should have different unknowns.

There are several different ways to carry out this activity. You can put strips of filter paper in test tubes rather than beakers. A single large piece of filter paper can be cut into a rectangle, spotted with the seven felt-tip markers, and then immersed in a beaker of water. Plastic containers can replace beakers for this activity. To save time, you may wish to divide each student group into subgroups and direct each subgroup to prepare chromatograms for one or two markers. The entire group will then use the full set of chromatograms to identify the unknown.

*(continued)*

## ADAPTATIONS FOR HIGH AND LOW ACHIEVERS

**High Achievers:** Discuss chromatography as a technique, including other types of chromatography and the basic principles that underlie them. You may also introduce the retention factor ($R_f$) and have higher-achieving students calculate the $R_f$ for each pigment in one of the inks. Also, encourage these students to do the follow-up activities, particularly activities 2, 3, and 5.

**Low Achievers:** Provide a glossary and reference material for boldfaced terms in this activity. Review the data table with these students and explain why this method is used to seperate pigments. Organize these students into cooperative learning groups, each of which should include students of higher ability.

## SCORING RUBRIC

Full credit should be given to students who record observations and answer all questions correctly, using full sentences. Extra credit should be given for completing follow-up activities.

 **INTERNET TIE-INS**

hhtp://www.yahoo.com/Science/Education/
http://www.chem.csustan.edu/chem1002/mrsketch.html
http://chem-inst-can.org/paper.html
http://chemistry.rutgers.edu/genchem/chrompap.html
http://chemistry.rutgers.edu/genchem/blackpen.html
http://thechalkboard.com/chalkboard/corporations/pharmacia_upjohn/Color/colorac4.html

 **QUIZ**
1. Explain how paper chromatography can be used to separate pigments.
2. What evidence can you provide that black ink is actually a mixture of several pigments?

Name_____ Date _____

# How Can We Separate Pigments?

 BEFORE YOU BEGIN

When you look at a sample of black ink, do you think of it as being a mixture of colors or a single color? In this activity, you will answer that question by using a technique called **paper chromatography** to separate the components of black ink. Paper chromatography is a way of separating a mixture into its components. In this case, the mixture is black ink. A spot of water-soluble ink is placed on a piece of filter paper, which acts as the **stationary phase**. The filter paper is then placed in water, which is the **mobile phase**; the water moves upward through the filter paper, carrying different pigments in the ink with it. Because the pigments have different physical and chemical properties, they move through the stationary phase differently and, therefore, they separate. The filter paper with its separated pigments is called a **chromatograph**.

 MATERIALS

- Two pieces of filter paper
- Eight black water-soluble felt-tip markers of different brands
- Eight pencils
- Scissors
- Eight beakers or other water containers
- Water in wash bottle
- Metric ruler
- Masking tape

## PROCEDURE

1. Cut eight strips of filter paper that measure 12 cm × 3 cm.

2. Trim each piece of filter paper that you cut to form a point at one end, as shown in the diagram. Make the points uniform on all eight strips.

3. Using the ruler and pencil, draw a line across each strip approximately 4 cm from the top. This is the "finish line." With a pencil, write the number "1" on the top of the first strip of filter paper above the finish line, as shown in the diagram. Write the number "2" on the next piece, number "3" on the third, etc., until all seven pieces of filter paper are numbered. The eighth piece of filter paper should be labeled "U" for "unknown."

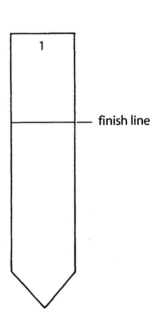

 finish line

*(continued)*

## How Can We Separate Pigments? *(continued)*

4. Using marker 1, draw a *horizontal line* across paper strip 1 just above where it starts to narrow to form a point, as shown.

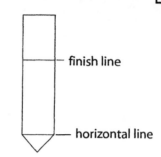

finish line

horizontal line

5. Use masking tape to stick the top of filter paper strip 1 to a pencil so that the pointed end hangs down, as indicated.

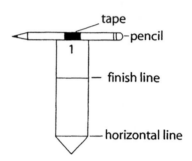

tape

pencil

finish line

horizontal line

6. Rest the pencil across the top of a beaker so that the paper strip hangs down into the beaker.

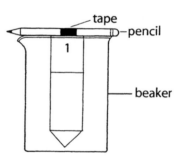

tape

pencil

beaker

7. Add enough water to the beaker to reach halfway between the pointed tip of the paper strip and the horizontal line.

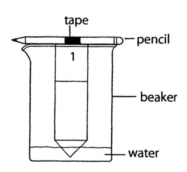

tape

pencil

beaker

water

8. Leave the paper strip in the water until the water travels up the strip to reach the finish line. Remove the paper strip. In the data table, record the colors that you see in the Data Collection and Analysis section.

9. Repeat steps 4–8 for each of the remaining numbered markers and for the unknown marker.

*(continued)*

## How Can We Separate Pigments? *(continued)*

 DATA COLLECTION AND ANALYSIS

### Data Table

| Marker Number | Colors in Chromatograph |
|---|---|
|  |  |
|  |  |
|  |  |
|  |  |
|  |  |
|  |  |
|  |  |
|  |  |

1. Which colors were found in all of the chromatographs?

   _____

   _____

   _____

2. Which marker(s) had the greatest number of colors in their chromatographs?

   _____

   _____

   _____

3. Which color traveled the farthest up the paper strip?

   _____

   _____

   _____

4. Which marker produced the most distinctive chromatograph?

   _____

   _____

   _____

5. On the back of this sheet, tape the seven chromatographs in numerical order.

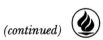

*(continued)*

## How Can We Separate Pigments? *(continued)*

### ❓ CONCLUDING QUESTIONS

1. Compare the chromatograph of the unknown marker with the chromatographs of the seven known markers. Identify the unknown marker. _____

_____

_____

2. Would this technique have worked with a marker containing water-insoluble ink? Why?

_____

_____

3. What factors determine the separation patterns produced by different inks? _____

_____

_____

4. What have you learned about black ink from this activity? _____

_____

_____

5. Are the pigments used to create black ink mixed by addition or subtraction? Explain your answer. _____

_____

_____

---

### 🎁 FOLLOW-UP ACTIVITIES 🎁

1. Suggest an experiment that would separate the pigments in water-insoluble inks.

2. Research and write a report about electrophoresis.

3. Research and write a report about gas chromatography.

4. Suggest an experiment to determine the colors present in the coatings of candy-coated m&m®-type chocolates.

5. The retention factor ($R_f$) of a pigment is calculated by dividing the distance the pigment moved by the distance the solvent moved. Determine the $R_f$ of each of the pigments in one of the seven chromatographs you prepared.

## INSTRUCTIONAL OBJECTIVES

Students will be able to

- record observations.
- calculate the magnification of a lens.
- describe the properties of magnifying lenses.
- evaluate experimental data and calculate the percentage error.
- draw conclusions based on observations.

 ## NATIONAL SCIENCE STANDARDS ADDRESSED

Students demonstrate understanding of

- magnifying lenses.
- interactions between light and matter.

Students demonstrate scientific inquiry and problem-solving skills by

- using physical science concepts to explain observations.
- identifying a problem and evaluating the outcomes of its investigation.
- evaluating accuracy, precision, and experimental design.
- working in teams to collect and share information and ideas.

Students demonstrate effective scientific communication by

- arguing from evidence.
- explaining scientific concepts to other students.

Students demonstrate competence with the tools and technologies of science by

- measuring with a metric ruler.
- working with lenses.
- analyzing data using concepts of accuracy, precision, and percentage error.

 ## MATERIALS

- Three double convex lenses, each with a different magnification (focal length)
- Five sheets of white paper
- Index card
- Scissors
- Newspaper
- Felt-tip marker
- Transparent tape
- Metric ruler

### HELPFUL HINTS AND DISCUSSION

**Time frame:** Two periods
**Structure:** Cooperative learning groups of three students
**Location:** In class

It is important to know the magnification or focal length of the lenses used in this activity and to give each student group three lenses with different magnifications (for example, 2X, 4X, 10X). You can purchase from scientific supply companies magnifying lenses with known magnification or double convex lenses with specified focal lengths. If you are using lenses with specified focal lengths, you can divide 25 by the focal length in cm to calculate magnification. Do not use lenses with focal lengths greater than 200 mm. If you do not have enough lenses with different focal lengths, you can combine two lenses by overlapping them to make a lens with a magnification equal to the two magnifications. The printed newspaper text that students use for this activity should be in type the size of column headlines. This activity is a good opportunity to introduce students to precision and accuracy as they discover variations in one another's measurements and deviations in the magnifications that they calculate from the accepted values for the lenses.

*(continued)*

## ADAPTATIONS FOR HIGH AND LOW ACHIEVERS

**High Achievers:** You may wish to explain how to calculate magnification from focal length and have these students calculate accepted values for magnification. Using the terms, explain the difference between precision and accuracy, and how we account for variance in each. Encourage these students to do the follow-up activities, particularly activities 1 and 3.

**Low Achievers:** Provide a glossary and reference material for bold-faced terms in this activity. Carefully review the data tables with these students. Explain that in Table II, the difference between accepted and experimental values may be *Column 1 minus Column 2* or *Column 2 minus Column 1* so the difference is a positive value. Discuss "precision" as a concept without using the term. Explain why three measurements of the magnified image are taken and why we use an average of the three measurements. Discuss "accuracy" as a concept and explain how we calculate percentage error. Review all calculations with lower-achieving students.

## SCORING RUBRIC

Full credit should be given to students who record observations and answer all questions, using full sentences. Extra credit should be given for completing follow-up activities.

 **INTERNET TIE-INS**

http://www.yahoo.com/science/education/
http://www.eecs.umich.edu
http://www.engr.csufresno.edu/~hadi/java/lenses/program.html
http://acept.la.asu.edu/Pin/act/microscopy/optical.shtml
http://www.kent.wednet.edu/staff/trobinso/physicspages/studyguide/ch26fldr/05.htm
http://www.topscience.org/

 **QUIZ**

1. What is the difference between a magnifying lens labeled 2X and one labeled 10X?
2. When an object with a measured height of 2.5 cm is viewed through a magnifying lens, its image has an apparent height of 7.5 cm. What is the magnification of this lens?

# How Can We Determine the Magnification of a Lens?

### 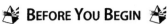 BEFORE YOU BEGIN

When you look through a magnifying lens, things look larger. The amount that the lens makes things appear larger is called the **magnification** of the lens. For example, a lens with a magnification of 2X will magnify an object to twice its actual size. In this activity, you will measure the magnification of three different magnifying lenses.

Because of the method we are using to find the magnification of these lenses, when different members of your laboratory group measure the same thing, their measurements may not be exactly the same. One way of working with such variation in measurement is to calculate an **average** of several measurements. To do this, you add the three measurements and then divide that sum by 3.

You will also compare the magnifications that you measure (experimental value) with accepted values for these lenses. The accepted value is the value provided by the lens manufacturer. You will determine the degree to which your measurement of magnification differs from the accepted values for these lenses. You will express this as the **percentage error**.

Percentage error is calculated using this formula:

$$\% \text{ error } = \frac{\text{accepted value} - \text{experimental value}}{\text{accepted value}} \times 100$$

##  MATERIALS

- Three double convex lenses, each with a different magnification (focal length)
- Five sheets of white paper
- Index card
- Scissors
- Newspaper
- Felt-tip marker
- Transparent tape
- Metric ruler

##  PROCEDURE

1. Cut one capital letter from a headline of a newspaper. Use transparent tape to paste this letter near one edge of an index card.

*(continued)*

## How Can We Determine the Magnification of a Lens? *(continued)*

2. Measure the height of the letter and record it in Data Table Ia, Col. 1, which is found in the Data Collection and Analysis section.

3. Place a piece of white paper on the desk in front of you and tape it to the desk. Place the index card on the piece of paper with the letter facing up.

4. Stand over the paper. Hold the first lens over the letter and raise the lens upward toward your eyes. Move the lens up and down until you find the point at which the image of the letter is focused and enlarged. You should note the distance above the paper at which you get the enlarged image in clearest focus.

5. With one eye looking through the lens at the image of the letter and the other eye looking at the paper, use a felt-tip marker to mark where you think the top and bottom of the image of the letter are on the paper. It may take several tries before you can look at the letter through the lens with one eye and at the paper with the other.

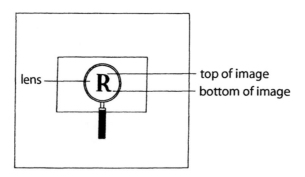

6. Use the ruler to measure the height of the image by measuring the distance between the two lines you marked on the paper. Record this measurement in Table Ia, Col. 2.

7. A second member of your lab team should repeat steps 3–6 and record the results in the second-try space in Table Ia.

8. A third member of your lab team should repeat steps 3–6. Record the results of the third-try space in Table Ia.

9. Repeat steps 3–8 with the second lens. Record all measurements in Data Table Ib.

10. Repeat steps 3–8 with the third lens. Record all measurements in Data Table Ic.

 **DATA COLLECTION AND ANALYSIS**

1. For each of the Data Tables (Ia, Ib, and Ic), calculate the magnifications for each lens by dividing column 2 by column 1.

2. For each Data Table (Ia–Ic), calculate the average magnification for the lens by adding up the three magnifications and dividing by 3. Record the number on the line below the table.

*(continued)*

## How Can We Determine the Magnification of a Lens? *(continued)*

### Data Table Ia, Lens 1

| Try | Col. 1<br>Actual Size of<br>Letter (in cm) | Col. 2<br>Magnified Size of<br>Letter (in cm) | Magnification<br>Calculated for<br>Lens 1<br>(col. 2 ÷ col. 1) |
|---|---|---|---|
| First try | | | |
| Second try | | | |
| Third try | | | |

Average Magnification of Lens 1= _____

### Data Table Ib, Lens 2

| Try | Col. 1<br>Actual Size of<br>Letter (in cm) | Col. 2<br>Magnified Size of<br>Letter (in cm) | Magnification<br>Calculated for<br>Lens 2<br>(col. 2 ÷ col. 1) |
|---|---|---|---|
| First try | | | |
| Second try | | | |
| Third try | | | |

Average Magnification of Lens 2= _____

### Data Table Ic, Lens 3

| Try | Col. 1<br>Actual Size of<br>Letter (in cm) | Col. 2<br>Magnified Size of<br>Letter (in cm) | Magnification<br>Calculated for<br>Lens 3<br>(col. 2 ÷ col. 1) |
|---|---|---|---|
| First try | | | |
| Second try | | | |
| Third try | | | |

Average Magnification of Lens 3= _____

3. Transfer the average magnifications for the three lenses to Data Table II, Col. 1.

4. Your teacher will tell you the accepted magnification values for the three lenses. Record this information in Table II, Col. 2.

5. Calculate the difference between the average measured values and accepted values for the three lenses. Enter these values in Table II.

*(continued)*

## How Can We Determine the Magnification of a Lens? *(continued)*

### Data Table II

| Lens | Col. 1<br>Average Measured<br>Magnification | Col. 2<br>Accepted Value<br>for Magnification | Difference<br>Between<br>Col. 1 & Col. 2 | % Error<br>(difference<br>÷ accepted<br>value × 100) |
|------|------|------|------|------|
|  |  |  |  |  |
|  |  |  |  |  |
|  |  |  |  |  |

6. For each lens in Data Table II, calculate the percentage error, using this formula:

$$\% \ error \ = \ \frac{accepted \ value - experimental \ value}{accepted \ value} \times 100$$

 ### CONCLUDING QUESTIONS

Record your answers to the following questions on the back of this sheet.

1. What does it mean when a magnifying lens is labeled 2X magnification?
2. Write a word equation for the calculation of magnification that you performed.
3. What are sources of error in this experiment?
4. How could you modify the procedures used in this activity to reduce the percentage error?
5. What is the purpose of calculating the percentage error for an experiment?

---

### 🔅 FOLLOW-UP ACTIVITIES 🔅

1. Another method for calculating magnification requires holding the lens above a piece of newsprint and raising the lens until you see a focused image. The distance from the newspaper to the lens when the image comes into focus is measured in centimeters. Divide 25 by this distance to calculate the magnification of the lens. Use this method to determine the magnification of a lens. Compare those results with the ones you obtained using the method in this activity.

2. With an eyedropper, place a drop of water on a piece of clear plastic wrap. Hold the plastic wrap over a piece of newspaper and look through the drop of water. Describe how looking through the drop of water affects what you see. Calculate the magnification of this "water" lens. Explain the magnifying effect of the drop of water.

3. Research and write a report on the use of lenses to correct nearsightedness and farsightedness.

4. Research and write a report on the use of lenses in microscopes and telescopes.

5. Investigate the magnification effects of looking at objects through a wineglass filled with water or a glass bottle filled with water. Explain the effects that you see.

---